LECTURES ON
ADVANCED NUMERICAL ANALYSIS

Notes on Mathematics and Its Applications

General Editors: Jacob T. Schwartz, Courant Institute of Mathematical Sciences, and Maurice Lévy, Université de Paris

E. Artin, ALGEBRAIC NUMBERS AND ALGEBRAIC FUNCTIONS
R. P. Boas, COLLECTED WORKS OF HIDEHIKO YAMABE
M. Davis, A FIRST COURSE IN FUNCTIONAL ANALYSIS
M. Davis, LECTURES ON MODERN MATHEMATICS
J. Eells, Jr., SINGULARITIES OF SMOOTH MAPS
K. O. Friedrichs, ADVANCED ORDINARY DIFFERENTIAL EQUATIONS
K. O. Friedrichs, SPECIAL TOPICS IN FLUID DYNAMICS
K. O. Friedrichs and H. N. Shapiro, INTEGRATION IN HILBERT SPACE
M. Hausner and J. T. Schwartz, LIE GROUPS; LIE ALGEBRAS
P. Hilton, HOMOTOPY THEORY AND DUALITY
F. John, LECTURES ON ADVANCED NUMERICAL ANALYSIS
H. Mullish, AN INTRODUCTION TO COMPUTER PROGRAMMING
F. Rellich, PERTURBATION THEORY
J. T. Schwartz, W* ALGEBRAS
A. Silverman, EXERCISES IN FORTRAN
J. J. Stoker, NONLINEAR ELASTICITY

Additional volumes in preparation

Lectures on Advanced Numerical Analysis

FRITZ JOHN
Courant Institute of Mathematical Sciences New York University

G|B
GORDON AND BREACH
SCIENCE PUBLISHERS NEW YORK · LONDON · PARIS

150 Fifth Avenue, New York, N.Y. 10011

Library of Congress Catalog Card Number: 66-26249

Distribution en France par:

Dunod Editeur
92 Rue Bonaparte
Paris 6, France

Distributed in Canada by:

The Ryerson Press
299 Queen Street West
Toronto 2B, Ontario

First published in Great Britain 1967

Printed in Belgium by
the Saint Catherine Press, Ltd., Tempelhof, Brugge

To Charlotte

General Preface

A large number of mathematical books begin as lecture notes; but, since mathematicians are busy, and since the labor required to bring lecture notes up to the level of perfection which authors and the public demand of formally published books is very considerable, it follows that an even larger number of lecture notes make the transition to book form only after great delay or not at all. The present lecture note series aims to fill the resulting gap. It will consist of reprinted lecture notes, edited at least to a satisfactory level of completeness and intelligibility, though not necessarily to the perfection which is expected of a book. In addition to lecture notes, the series will include volumes of collected reprints of journal articles as current developments indicate, and mixed volumes including both notes and reprints.

JACOB T. SCHWARTZ
MAURICE LÉVY

Preface

These *Lectures on Numerical Analysis* are essentially lectures notes of a course on "Advanced Numerical Methods" which the author gave in 1956-57 at the Institute of Mathematical Sciences at New York University. The original notes, prepared by S. d'Ambra and S. Locke, were distributed by the Institute for a number of years in mimeographed form. The author has made extensive revisions in the wording of theorems and proofs and the list of references, but had to refrain from making the major changes that would be required in an attempt to bring the material up to date. It has not always been possible to perfect the informal style of the original notes.

It is hoped that even in its present form the book can serve as an introduction to the field for students who have a fair knowledge of linear algebra, of functions of a complex variable, and of the basic facts about ordinary and partial differential equations.

FRITZ JOHN

June 1966

Contents

Chapter 1

MATRIX INVERSION

Chapter 2

SOLUTIONS OF NON-LINEAR EQUATIONS AND SYSTEMS OF EQUATIONS

Chapter 3

Approximation of Eigenvalues of a Matrix

Chapter 4

Approximation of Functions

Chapter 5

SOLUTION OF ORDINARY DIFFERENTIAL EQUATIONS

Chapter 6

THE HEAT EQUATION

Chapter 7

THE WAVE EQUATION

CHAPTER 1

Matrix Inversion*

1. Systems of Linear Equations in Matrix Notation

The basic problem considered is that of solving a set of n equations in n unknowns.

$$\sum_{k=1}^{n} a_{ik} x_k = y_i \qquad (i = 1, \cdots, n). \tag{1.1}$$

We can always find a solution by Cramer's Rule if the matrix of coefficients has a determinant not equal to zero. The solution is given by:

$$x_i = \frac{\begin{vmatrix} a_{11} & \cdots & a_{1i-1} & y_1 & a_{1i+1} & \cdots & a_{1n} \\ \cdots & \cdots & \cdots & \cdots & \cdots & \cdots & \cdots \\ a_{n1} & \cdots & a_{ni-1} & y_n & a_{ni+1} & \cdots & a_{nn} \end{vmatrix}}{\begin{vmatrix} a_{11} & \cdots & a_{1i-1} & a_{1i} & a_{1i-1} & \cdots & a_{1n} \\ \cdots & \cdots & \cdots & \cdots & \cdots & \cdots & \cdots \\ a_{n1} & \cdots & a_{ni+1} & a_{ni} & a_{ni+1} & \cdots & a_{nn} \end{vmatrix}}. \tag{1.2}$$

We shall use vertical lines to indicate a determinant. Curved brackets will denote matrices or vectors. We will use lower case letters to denote matrices and vectors when we don't want to write out the subscripts.

Hence:

$$a = \begin{pmatrix} a_{11} a_{12} & \cdots & a_{1n} \\ a_{21} \cdots & & \\ \cdots & & \\ a_{n1} & & a_{nn} \end{pmatrix}, \qquad x = \begin{pmatrix} x_1 \\ \vdots \\ x_n \end{pmatrix} \qquad y = \begin{pmatrix} y_1 \\ \vdots \\ y_n \end{pmatrix}.$$

---

* See Householder [21, 22], Hildebrand [19], Newmant [33], Antosiewicz and Rheinboldt [2].

We denote the conjugate transposed of a by a^*, similarly for x^* and y^*. We write $|a|$ for the determinant of the matrix a.
In this notation our system of equations (1) becomes

$$y = ax$$

and our solution becomes

$$x = a^{-1}y.$$

In principle this solution can be found by Cramer's Rule, evaluating the determinants as sums of products. However, in practice this leads to a number of difficulties:

(a) The given quantities a_{ik}, y_k may not be known exactly. In any case, they have to be rounded off before being used in a digital computer. Thus, at best, instead of the actual system an approximate system is solved.

(b) This approximate system can itself not be solved exactly by machines. For instance, division, which is involved in the solution, can only be carried to a finite number of places.

(c) It may not be feasible to obtain an approximate solution to the approximate system in the way described by Cramer's Rule, since the number of steps involved may be too large. Cruder approximate solution schemes, e.g. iteration, may be preferable.

Therefore, it is important to be able to estimate the error involved when instead of an exact solution to a given system of equations one only obtains an approximate solution to an approximate system of equations.

2. Norms of Vectors

In order to estimate errors in computed values of vectors and matrices, it is convenient to have a measure of the "magnitude" of a vector or matrix. Norms are suitable measures. The set of vectors considered forms a linear vector space: given vectors x and y of the same dimensions and a scalar λ, then $x + y$ and λx are vectors. We will restrict λ either to real or complex numbers.

A function on the members x of a linear vector space X whose values are real numbers is called a *norm* if it satisfies the following conditions

$$N(x) \geqslant 0 \qquad \text{for all } x \text{ in } X$$

$$N(x) = 0 \qquad \text{if and only if} \qquad x = 0 \tag{2.1}$$

$$N(\lambda x) = |\lambda| N(x) \qquad \text{for all } x \text{ in } X \text{ and all scalars } \lambda \tag{2.2}$$

$$N(x + y) \leqslant N(x) + N(y) \qquad \text{for all } x \text{ and } y \text{ in } X. \tag{2.3}$$

Examples of norms of vector spaces are:

$$N_2(x) = [|x_1|^2 + \cdots + |x_n|^2]^{1/2} \tag{2.4}$$

$$N_\infty(x) = \text{Max } |x_i| \qquad (i = 1, \cdots, n) \tag{2.5}$$

$$N_1(x) = \sum_i |x_i|. \tag{2.6}$$

N_2 has the advantage that its square is differentiable for real numbers. (2.4), (2.5) and (2.6) are special cases of

$$N_P(x) = \left[\sum_{i=1}^{n} |x_i|^P\right]^{1/P} \qquad P \geqslant 1. \tag{2.7}$$

This satisfies (2.1) and (2.2) trivially. That it satisfies (2.3) follows from Minkowski's inequality.[1]

These norms N_P give the same weight to all components of vector x. Norms which are not symmetric functions of the components can be obtained as follows from a given norm N:

Let T be a non-singular square matrix. We can define a new norm of x by $N(Tx)$. It is easy to verify that this is a norm. Our N_2, for example, in inner product notation is:

$$N_2(x) = \sqrt{x * x}. \tag{2.8}$$

We can define then a norm $N(x)$ by

$$\begin{aligned} N(x) &= N_2(Tx) \\ &= \sqrt{x * T * Tx} \\ &= \sqrt{x * Bx} \end{aligned} \tag{2.9}$$

where $B = T * T$ is a definite hermitian matrix.

---

[1] See Hardy-Littlewood-Polya [14], p. 30.

Any two norms $N(x)$ and $N'(x)$ are 'equivalent' in the sense that there exist positive numbers m and M such that

$$mN'(x) \leqslant N(x) \leqslant MN'(x). \tag{2.10}$$

Proof: Since two norms 'equivalent' to a third are 'equivalent' to each other it is sufficient to show that any norm is 'equivalent' to $N_\infty(x)$. For any vector x with components x_i we have

$$x = \sum_{i=1}^{n} x_i e^i, \qquad e^i = (0, 0, \cdots, 1, 0, \cdots, 0)^*$$

Then

$$N(x) \leqslant \sum_i | x_i | N(e^i) \leqslant N_\infty(x) \sum_i N(e^i) = MN_\infty(x)$$

where $M = \Sigma_i N(e^i)$. It follows that $N(x)$ is a continuous function of $x_1, \cdots, x_n$: Indeed, by (2.3)

$$N(y) \leqslant N(x) + N(y - x) = N(x) + N(x - y)$$
$$N(x) \leqslant N(y) + N(x - y)$$

and hence

$$| N(y) - N(x) | \leqslant N(x - y) \leqslant MN_\infty(x - y) = M \operatorname{Max}_i | x_i - y_i |.$$

Thus $N(x)$ attains its minimum m on the compact set $N_\infty(x) = 1$ at a point x^0:

$$N(x) \geqslant N(x^0) = m \qquad \text{for} \qquad N_\infty(x) = 1.$$

Here $m > 0$ since $x^0 \neq 0$. It follows that for any $x \neq 0$

$$N(x) = N\left(N_\infty(x) \frac{1}{N_\infty(x)} x\right) = N_\infty(x) N\left(\frac{1}{N_\infty(x)} x\right) \geqslant mN_\infty(x)$$

which completes the proof.

For example

$$N_\infty(x) \leqslant N_2(x) \leqslant \sqrt{n}\, N_\infty(x) \tag{2.11}$$

$$N_\infty(x) \leqslant N_1(x) \leqslant nN_\infty(x). \tag{2.12}$$

In particular if for a sequence of vectors one type of norm tends to zero all types tend to zero.

3. Norm of a Matrix

There are several ways to define the norm of a matrix. We can simply consider the matrices as forming a new linear vector space of dimension n^2. This leads for instance to the norms:

$$\tilde{N}_2(a) = \left[\sum_{\substack{i=1\\k=1}}^{n} | a_{ik} |^2 \right]^{1/2} \tag{3.1}$$

$$\tilde{N}_1(a) = \sum_{\substack{i=1\\k=1}}^{n} | a_{ik} | . \tag{3.2}$$

However: once we have defined a norm $N(x)$ for the vectors x it is more natural to define a corresponding norm $N(a)$ for matrices a [as is generally done for linear operators] by:

$$N(a) = \text{l.u.b.} \frac{N(ax)}{N(x)} \quad \text{for all possible} \quad x \neq 0. \tag{3.3}$$

Here l.u.b. means least upper bound or "supremum." With this definition we obtain the following properties for $N(a)$:

$$N(ax) \leqslant N(a)\, N(x). \tag{3.4}$$

Proof:

$$N(a) = \text{l.u.b.}_{x \neq 0} \frac{N(ax)}{N(x)}$$

implies

$$N(a) \geqslant \frac{N(ax)}{N(x)} \quad \text{for any} \quad x \neq 0.$$

Hence

$$N(x)\, N(a) \geqslant N(ax)$$

Q.E.D.

$$N(ab) \leqslant N(a)\, N(b). \tag{3.5}$$

Proof:

$$N(abx) = N(a(bx)) \leqslant N(a)\,N(bx) \leqslant N(a)\,N(b)\,N(x)$$

by repeated application of (3.4). Hence

$$\frac{N(abx)}{N(x)} \leqslant N(a)\,N(b) \qquad \text{for all} \qquad x \neq 0$$

$$\underset{x\neq 0}{\text{l.u.b.}}\,\frac{N(abx)}{N(x)} = N(ab) \leqslant N(a)\,N(b)$$

Q.E.D.

$$N(a+b) \leqslant N(a) + N(b). \tag{3.6}$$

Proof:

$$N((a+b)\,x) = N(ax+bx) \leqslant N(ax) + N(bx)$$

from property (2.3) of norms of vectors. Here by (3.4)

$$N(ax) + N(bx) \leqslant N(a)\,N(x) + N(b)\,N(x).$$

Thus

$$\frac{N[(a+b)\,x]}{N(x)} \leqslant N(a) + N(b) \qquad \text{for all} \qquad x \neq 0$$

$$\text{l.u.b.}\,\frac{N[(a+b)\,x]}{N(x)} = N(a+b) \leqslant N(a) + N(b).$$

Q.E.D.

$$N(\lambda a) = |\,\lambda\,|\,N(a). \tag{3.7}$$

Proof: By (2.2)

$$N(\lambda ax) = |\,\lambda\,|\,N(ax)$$

$$\underset{x\neq 0}{\text{l.u.b.}}\,\frac{N(\lambda ax)}{N(x)} = \underset{x\neq 0}{\text{l.u.b.}}\,\frac{|\,\lambda\,|\,N(ax)}{N(x)}$$

$$N(\lambda a) = |\,\lambda\,|\,N(a)$$

Q.E.D.

$$N(a) \geqslant 0 \qquad \text{for all } a$$

$$N(a) = 0 \qquad \text{if and only if} \qquad a = 0. \tag{3.8}$$

Proof: $\text{l.u.b.}_{x \neq 0} N(ax)/N(x)$ is the l.u.b. of a set of non-negative numbers and is therefore $\geqslant 0$. If $a = 0$ then $ax = 0$ and

$$\frac{N(ax)}{N(x)} = 0 \qquad \text{for all} \qquad x \neq 0$$

that is

$$N(a) = 0.$$

Conversely $N(a) = 0$ implies $N(ax)/N(x) = 0$ for all $x \neq 0$. Then $ax = 0$ for every x and therefore $a = 0$.

Q.E.D.

Formulae (3.6), (3.7), and (3.8) assure us that $N(a)$ is a norm in the space of matrices. We shall call norms for matrices defined by (3.3) *natural norms.*

We will call the unit matrix I. Since $Ix = x$ for all x we have (for any natural norm)

$$N(I) = 1. \tag{3.9}$$

If μ_i are the eigen values of a we have

$$ax = \mu_i x \qquad \text{for some} \qquad x \neq 0.$$

Then for natural norms

$$N(ax) = N(\mu_i x) = |\mu_i| N(x)$$

$$\frac{N(ax)}{N(x)} = |\mu_i| \qquad \text{for some} \qquad x \neq 0.$$

It follows that

$$\text{l.u.b.} \frac{N(ax)}{N(x)} = N(a) \geqslant |\mu_i|.$$

Consequently

$$N(a) \geqslant \text{Max} |\mu_i| \qquad (i = 1, \cdots n). \tag{3.10}$$

To show that the equality sign in (3.10) does not always hold we consider the matrix

$$a = \begin{pmatrix} 1 & 1 \\ 0 & 1 \end{pmatrix} \qquad \text{where} \qquad |\mu_1| = |\mu_2| = 1$$

for which

$$a = I + E \qquad \text{where} \qquad E = \begin{pmatrix} 0 & 1 \\ 0 & 0 \end{pmatrix}.$$

Here $E^2 = 0$. Consequently, by the binomial theorem,

$$a^k = I + kE$$

and

$$\frac{1}{k}(a^k - I) = E.$$

Therefore by (3.6), (3.7), (3.4), (3.9)

$$N(E) = N\left[\frac{1}{k}(a^k - I)\right] \leqslant \frac{1}{k}[N(a^k) + N(I)] \leqslant \frac{1}{k}[N(a)^k + 1].$$

Now assume $N(a) \leqslant 1$ then $N(a)^k \leqslant 1$ and $N(E) \leqslant 2/k$; now k is arbitrary and $2/k \to 0$ as $k \to \infty$. Hence $N(E) = 0$.

This cannot be true since $E \neq 0$; therefore our assumption $N(a) \leqslant 1$ is false and

$$N(a) > 1 = \max_i |\mu_i|.$$

However we have:

Theorem. For any given matrix a_0 with eigenvalues μ_i and any $\epsilon > 0$ a natural norm $N(a)$ can be found such that

$$N(a_0) \leqslant \operatorname{Max} |\mu_i| + \epsilon. \tag{3.11}$$

To prove this we shall use some properties of matrices. There exists a non-singular matrix T such that $a_0 = T^{-1}\alpha T$ where α is a triangular matrix (for example the Jordan canonical form of a_0)

$$\alpha = \begin{pmatrix} \mu_1 & \alpha_{12} & \cdots & \alpha_{1n} \\ & \mu_2 & . & \vdots \\ & & \ddots & \vdots \\ & & & \mu_n \end{pmatrix}.$$

I assert we can make the off diagonal members in α as small as we wish by transforming as follows: Define S as the diagonal matrix

$$S = \begin{pmatrix} 1 & & \cdots & 0 \\ \vdots & \delta & \cdot & \\ \cdot & 0 & \ddots & \delta^{n-1} \end{pmatrix}$$

then

$$\sigma = S^{-1}\alpha S = \begin{pmatrix} \mu_1 & \delta a_{12} & \delta^2 a_{13} & \cdots & \delta^{n-1}a_{1n} \\ 0 & \mu_2 & \delta a_{23} & \cdots & \delta^{n-2}a_{2n} \\ \cdots & \cdots & \cdots & \cdots & \cdots \\ 0 & 0 & 0 & \cdots & \delta a_{n-1n} \\ 0 & 0 & 0 & \cdots & \mu_n \end{pmatrix}$$

where obviously since δ is arbitrary the off diagonal members can be made arbitrarily small. Let $\sigma = \Lambda + \beta$. Then β has arbitrarily small elements and Λ is the diagonal matrix $\Lambda = \begin{pmatrix} \mu_1 & 0 \\ 0 & \mu_n \end{pmatrix}$. We have $a_0 = T^{-1}S\sigma S^{-1}T$. Consider the norm

$$N(x) = N_2(S^{-1}Tx) = \sqrt{x^*T^*S^{-1*}S^{-1}Tx}.$$

Set $S^{-1}Tx = y$; then

$$N(x) = \sqrt{y^*y}$$

$$N(a_0x) = \sqrt{x^*a_0{}^*T^*S^{-1*}S^{-1}Ta_0x}\,.$$

We have

$$S^{-1}Ta_0 = \sigma S^{-1}T.$$

Hence

$$\begin{aligned} N(a_0x) &= \sqrt{y^*\sigma^*\sigma y} \\ \sigma^*\sigma &= (\Lambda^* + \beta^*)(\Lambda + \beta) \\ &= \Lambda^*\Lambda + \gamma \end{aligned}$$

where γ is arbitrarily small. Then

$$\frac{N(a_0x)}{N(x)} = \sqrt{\frac{y^*\Lambda^*\Lambda y + y^*\gamma y}{y^*y}}$$

$$= \frac{\sqrt{\sum_{k=1}^{n} |\mu_k|^2 |y_k|^2 + \sum_{\substack{i=1 \\ k=1}}^{n} \gamma_{ik}\bar{y}_i y_k}}{\sqrt{\sum_{k=1}^{n} |y_k|^2}}$$

Now

$$|y_i|\,|y_k| \leqslant \sum_{i=1}^{n} |y_i|^2$$

$$\sum_{\substack{i=1\\k=1}}^{n} \gamma_{ik}\bar{y}_i y_k \leqslant \Big(\sum_{\substack{i=1\\k=1}}^{n} |\gamma_{ik}|\Big)\Big(\sum_{i=1}^{n} |y_i|^2\Big) \leqslant \epsilon \sum_{i=1}^{n} |y_i|^2$$

where ϵ is arbitrarily small. Therefore

$$\frac{N(a_0x)}{N(x)} \leqslant \sqrt{\frac{\Big(\sum_{i=1}^{n} |\mu_i|^2 + \epsilon\Big)|y_i|^2}{\sum_i |y_i|^2}}$$

$$\leqslant \sqrt{\max_{i=1\ldots n} |\mu_i|^2 + \epsilon}$$

$$\leqslant \max_{i=1\ldots n} |\mu_i| + \epsilon^*$$

with ϵ^* arbitrarily small which was to be shown.

Theorem. A necessary and sufficient condition for a matrix a to be such that $\mathrm{Lim}_{k\to\infty}\, a^k = 0$ is that for all i we have

$$|\mu_i| < 1$$

Proof: Let μ be an eigenvalue and x an eigenvector:

$$ax = \mu x$$

then

$$a^k x = \mu^k x.$$

Therefore

$$N(a^k x) = N(\mu^k x) = |\mu|^k N(x)$$

$$\text{l.u.b.}\,\frac{N(a^k x)}{N(x)} = N(a^k) \geqslant |\mu|^k.$$

Hence if $N(a^k) \to 0$, also $|\mu|^k \to 0$ and this implies $|\mu| < 1$.

Conversely if all $|\mu_i| < 1$ then Max $|\mu_i| < 1$ and from theorem (3.11) we can choose an $\epsilon < (1 - \text{Max} |\mu_i|)$ and a natural norm N such that

$$N(a) \leqslant \text{Max} |\mu_i| + \epsilon < 1$$

$$N(a) = q < 1 .$$

Then

$$N(a^k) \leqslant (N(a))^k = q^k$$

and as $k \to \infty$, $q^k \to 0$ and $N(a^k) \to 0$.

Using Lemma (2.10) this implies that $a^k \to 0$.

4. Special Natural Norms for Matrices

We shall construct the norms $N_\infty(a)$ and $N_2(a)$ on the basis of the general definition for natural norms. We have

$$N_\infty(x) = \operatorname*{Max}_i |x_i| .$$

Then

$$N_\infty(ax) = \operatorname*{Max}_i \left| \sum_k a_{ik} x_k \right| \leqslant N_\infty(x) \operatorname*{Max}_i \sum_k |a_{ik}| .$$

The equal sign holds for $x_k = |a_{ik}|/a_{ik}$ where i is that value for which $\Sigma_k |a_{ik}|$ is largest. Hence

$$N_\infty(a) = \operatorname*{Max}_i \sum_k |a_{ik}| . \tag{4.1}$$

We have

$$N_2(x) = \left(\sum_i |x_i|^2\right)^{1/2} = (x^*x)^{1/2} .$$

Therefore

$$\frac{N_2(ax)}{N_2(x)} = \frac{(x^*a^*ax)^{1/2}}{(x^*x)^{1/2}} = \frac{x^*bx^{1/2}}{(x^*x)^{1/2}}$$

where $b = a^*a$.

We have for any eigenvalue λ of b an $x \neq 0$ such that

$$bx = \lambda x$$

$$x^*bx = \lambda x^*x$$

$$\lambda = \frac{x^*bx}{x^*x} = \frac{N_2(ax)^2}{N_2(x)^2}.$$

Therefore λ is real and non-negative. Since b is hermitian $(b^* = b)$, there exists a unitary matrix T, $(T^*T = I)$ such that

$$b = T^*\Lambda T$$

where Λ is a diagonal matrix with the eigenvalues λ_k of b on the main diagonal, i.e.

$$\lambda = \begin{pmatrix} \lambda_1 & 0 & \cdots & 0 \\ 0 & \lambda_2 & \cdots & 0 \\ \vdots & \vdots & \ddots & \vdots \\ 0 & 0 & & \lambda_n \end{pmatrix}.$$

Then if we define a new arbitrary vector y by $y = Tx$ we have $x = T^*y$ and

$$\frac{N_2(ax)}{N_2(x)} = \frac{(y^*TbT^*y)^{1/2}}{(y^*TT^*y)^{1/2}} = \frac{(y^*\Lambda y)^{1/2}}{(y^*y)^{1/2}}$$

$$= \frac{\left(\sum \lambda_i \mid y_i \mid^2\right)^{1/2}}{\left(\sum_i \mid y_i \mid^2\right)^{1/2}} \leqslant \sqrt{\operatorname{Max}_i \mid \lambda_i \mid}\,.$$

If λ_i is the largest eigenvalue then the equality holds for a vector y with components δ_{ij} . Therefore

$$N_2(a)^2 = \left(\text{l.u.b.}\, \frac{N_2(ax)}{N_2(x)}\right)^2 = \operatorname{Max}_k \lambda_k\,. \tag{4.2}$$

If perchance a happens to be hermitian the eigenvalues of a^*a are the squares of the eigenvalues of a. In this case

$$N_2(a) = \operatorname{Max}_k \mid \mu_k \mid, \tag{4.3}$$

where the μ_k are the eigenvalues of a.

Unfortunately it is usually very difficult to find the eigenvalues of a matrix. We can estimate $N_2(a)$ by a simpler expression. The trace of b is

$$\operatorname{Tr} b = \sum_i b_{ii} = \sum_i \lambda_i = \operatorname{Tr}(a^*a).$$

Therefore

$$n \operatorname*{Max}_i \lambda_i \geqslant \operatorname{Tr} b \geqslant \operatorname*{Max}_i \lambda_i \tag{4.4}$$

but since $b = a^*a$

$$b_{ik} = \sum_j (\overline{a_{ji}})(a_{jk})$$

we have

$$\operatorname{Tr} b = \sum_i \sum_j (\overline{a_{ji}})(a_{ji}) = \sum_{i,j} | a_{ji} |^2.$$

Now we defined in (3.1)

$$\tilde{N}_2(a) = \Big(\sum_{i,j} | a_{ij} |^2\Big)^{1/2}$$

which is easier to calculate than $N_2(a)$. We have then from (4.4)

$$\frac{1}{\sqrt{n}} \tilde{N}_2(a) \leqslant N_2(a) \leqslant \tilde{N}_2(a). \tag{4.5}$$

5. Estimate of the Error due to Approximating the Equations

Although our aim is to solve $ax = y$ we have explained that it is generally only possible to solve an approximate system $Ax = Y$ approximately. Let X be an assumed close solution. Then

$$AX = Y + Z \tag{5.1}$$

where Z is a correction term. Suppose we have A, X, Y and Z and, moreover estimates for $N(a - A)$ and $N(y - Y)$. We then wish to estimate $x - X$ or, what is equivalent, $N(x - X)$. Incidentally, N is assumed to be a natural norm.

Writing the basic equation as

$$(A + (a - A))\,(X + (x - X)) = Y + (y - Y)$$

we arrive at

$$x - X = A^{-1}[- Z + (y - Y) - (a - A)\,(x - X) - (a - A)\,X].$$

Taking the norms we have

$$N(x - X) \leqslant N(A^{-1})\,[N(Z) + N(y - Y) + N(a - A)\,N(x - X) + N(a - A)\,N(X)].$$

Solving for $N(x - X)$ we have the desired estimate

$$N(x - X) \leqslant \frac{N(A^{-1})\,[N(Z) + N(y - Y) + N(a - A)\,N(X)]}{1 - N(A^{-1})\,N(a - A)} \tag{5.2}$$

provided the denominator is still positive. But we must know $N(A^{-1})$ to in order to bound our error. This is not as easily accomplished as finding estimates of $N(a)$ and will be discussed in the next paragraph.

6. Estimates for the Norm of the Reciprocal of a Matrix

Formally a^{-1} is given by $a^{-1} = (A_{ki}/|\,a\,|)$ where the A_{ik} are the cofactors of the elements a_{ik} of a. Then in particular we have

$$N_\infty(a^{-1}) = \operatorname*{Max}_i \frac{1}{|\,a\,|} \sum_k |\,A_{ki}\,|\,. \tag{6.1}$$

It is easily shown that

$$N_2(a^{-1}) = \frac{1}{(\operatorname*{Min}_i \lambda_i)^{1/2}} \tag{6.2}$$

where λ_i is, as before, an eigenvalue of a^*a or of aa^*. Unfortunately, these expressions require extensive calculation and as a result are not always computable.

It is sometimes possible to determine an upper bound for $N(a^{-1})$, if we have an approximation for a^{-1}, say a matrix c; let

$$I - ca = r$$

where r gives a measure of the deviation of c from a^{-1}. It is necessary to require $N(r) < 1$. Then

$$(I - ca)\, a^{-1} = a^{-1} - c = ra^{-1}$$

$$a^{-1} = c + ra^{-1}$$

$$N(a^{-1}) \leqslant N(c) + N(r)\, N(a^{-1})$$

$$N(a^{-1})\, [1 - N(r)] \leqslant N(c)$$

and our final result is

$$N(a^{-1}) \leqslant \frac{N(c)}{1 - N(r)}; \qquad N(r) < 1. \tag{6.3}$$

As an illustration we let $a = \alpha + \beta$ where α is the matrix of the diagonal elements of a. Then we can take for c the matrix α^{-1}. Here

$$r = I - ca$$
$$= I - \alpha^{-1}(\alpha + \beta) = -\alpha^{-1}\beta. \tag{6.4}$$

Then our bound is

$$N(a^{-1}) \leqslant \frac{N(\alpha^{-1})}{1 - N(\alpha^{-1}\beta)}$$

if $N(\alpha^{-1}\beta) < 1$. Carrying out this calculation we start with

$$\alpha_{ik} = a_{ik}\delta_{ik}; \qquad \beta_{ik} = a_{ik}(1 - \delta_{ik}).$$

Then

$$-r = \alpha^{-1}\beta = \left(\frac{1}{a_{ik}}\,\delta_{ik}\right)\left(a_{ik}(1 - \delta_{ik})\right)$$

$$= \left(\sum_{l} \frac{1}{a_{il}}\,\delta_{il}a_{lk}(1 - \delta_{lk})\right)$$

which implies that

$$r_{ik} = \begin{cases} -\dfrac{a_{ik}}{a_{ii}} & i \neq k \\ 0 & i = k. \end{cases}$$

Therefore, for instance,

$$N_\infty(\alpha^{-1}\beta) = \operatorname*{Max}_i \frac{1}{|a_{ii}|} \sum_{k \neq i} |a_{ik}| . \tag{6.5}$$

Let, e.g.

$$\sum_{k \neq i} |a_{ik}| \leqslant q \operatorname*{Min}_i |a_{ii}|$$

where $q < 1$. In this case we have

$$N_\infty(\alpha^{-1}b) \leqslant q.$$

Since

$$N_\infty(\alpha^{-1}) = \operatorname*{Max}_i \frac{1}{|a_{ii}|}$$

our estimate is

$$N_\infty(a^{-1}) \leqslant \frac{\operatorname*{Max}_i \dfrac{1}{|a_{ii}|}}{1-q} .$$

However the whole procedure is based on the assumption that a can be approximated sufficiently well by a diagonal matrix.

7. Matrix Inversion by Successive Approximations

We shall now describe a general method of attacking two related problems utilizing iteration methods. When these apply, estimates are obtained without too much difficulty.

Problem (a). Given a find a^{-1} and solve $ax = y$ for any y utilizing $x = a^{-1}y$.

Problem (b). Given a and y find $a^{-1}y$ without finding a^{-1} first.

We shall consider (a) first. We start with an approximation c to a^{-1} such that

$$I - ca = r$$

as before. Multiplying by a^{-1} from the right yields

$$a^{-1} = c + ra^{-1}. \tag{7.1}$$

We shall define a sequence of matrices c_n by

$$c_{n+1} = c + rc_n \,. \tag{7.2}$$

where c_0 is an arbitrary matrix, for instance $c_0 = 0$. The error after n steps is s_n where

$$s_n = a^{-1} - c_n \tag{7.3}$$

Then from (7.1) and (7.2)

$$\begin{aligned} s_n &= (a^{-1} - c) - rc_{n-1} = ra^{-1} - rc_{n-1} \\ &= rs_{n-1} \end{aligned}$$

with the result that

$$s_n = r^n s_0 \,. \tag{7.4}$$

Therefore a necessary and sufficient condition for the convergence of c_n for arbitrary c_0 is that $r^n \to 0$. This will happen if, and only if, all the eigenvalues of r are less than one in absolute value.

A sufficient condition for $r^n \to 0$ with any norm is that $N(r) = q < 1$. This is so because $N(r)$ is not exceeded by the absolute value of any eigenvalue of r. (See (3.10), p. 7)

It follows from (7.4) that

$$a^{-1} - c_n = r^n(a^{-1} - c_n)$$

which implies

$$N(a^{-1} - c_n) \leqslant q^n[N(a^{-1}) + N(c_0)].$$

By 6.3 this result becomes

$$N(a^{-1} - c_n) \leqslant q^n \left[\frac{N(c)}{1 - q} + N(c_0)\right] \tag{7.5}$$

which provides a concrete error estimate.

8. Effect of Rounding off

In practice we have due to rounding off a sequence c_n satisfying, instead of (7.2), a recursion formula

$$c_{n+1} = c + rc_n + \epsilon_n \tag{8.1}$$

with an intermediate error ϵ_n. Let it be known that $N(\epsilon_n) < \epsilon$. Then putting again $s_n = a^{-1} - c_n$ we find by the same substitutions

$$s_{n+1} = rs_n - \epsilon_n . \tag{8.2}$$

This means

$$N(s_{n+1}) \leqslant N(r)\, N(s_n) + N(\epsilon_n).$$

Remembering $N(r) = q$ and iterating

$$\begin{aligned} N(s_{n+1}) &\leqslant qN(s_n) + \epsilon \\ \vdots \qquad & \quad \vdots \\ &\leqslant q^{n+1}N(s_0) + \epsilon\,\frac{(1 - q^{n+1})}{1 - q} . \end{aligned}$$

Therefore

$$N(s_n) \leqslant \frac{\epsilon}{1 - q} + q^n N(s_0). \tag{8.3}$$

Here all we can say is that as $n \to \infty$ the lim. sup. of our error is bounded by $\epsilon/(1 - q)$. A reasonable value of n to take is one for which $q^n N(s_c) \sim \epsilon/(1 - q)$ where the total error is about twice the optimum value.

Problem (a). Treated by formula (7.2) requires n^3 multiplications for each iteration step.

Problem (b). Which will be treated analogously however requires only n^2 multiplications for each iteration step.

9. Solution of Systems of Linear Equations by Successive Approximations

For $x = a^{-1}y$ we want to find an approximate x using the above methods and sequence c_n as a guide. If $x^k = c_k y$ where $c_{k+1} = c + rc_k$ we have

$$x^{k+1} = cy + rx^k . \tag{9.1}$$

We can define a sequence x^k directly by this recursion formula. Actually we will have an error δ_k such that

$$x^{k+1} = cy + rx^k + \delta_k \tag{9.2}$$

where $N(\delta_k) < \delta$. We take x^0 arbitrary. Since the true solution is $x = cy + rx$ we find by subtraction

$$x - x^{k+1} = r(x - x^k) - \delta_k .$$

Taking norms and iterating, the final result becomes

$$N(x - x^k) \leqslant q^k N(x - x^0) + \delta \left(\frac{1 - q^k}{1 - q}\right).$$

For $q < 1$ the error may be as high as $\delta/(1 - q)$. If $x_0 = 0$,

$$N(x - x^0) = N(a^{-1}y) \leqslant \frac{N(c)}{1 - q} N(y) . \tag{9.3}$$

10. Successive Approximations Using a Partial Inverse of the Matrix

We continue solving $ax = y$ by iteration methods.

Let us split the matrix a into $a = \alpha - \beta$ where α is more readily inverted than a. Now consider $c = \alpha^{-1}$

$$I - ca = - (\alpha^{-1}\beta) = r.$$

By (9.1)

$$x^{k+1} = \alpha^{-1}y - (\alpha^{-1}\beta)\, x^k .$$

Multiplying by α on the left yields

$$\alpha x^{k+1} + \beta x^k = y. \tag{10.1}$$

The x^k will converge if $\alpha^{-1}\beta$ has all its eigenvalues inside the unit circle.

There are two cases we shall consider: (1) α consists of the diagonal elements of a; and (2) α consists of the elements of a on and below the diagonal (Gauss-Seidel scheme).

In case (1) our set of equations (10.1) written out is

$$\begin{aligned} a_{11}x_1^{k+1} + a_{12}x_2^k + \cdots + a_{in}x_n^k &= y_1 \\ a_{21}x_1^k + a_{22}x_2^{k+1} + \cdots \qquad\qquad &= y_2 \\ a_{n1}x_1^k + a_{n2}x_2^k + \cdots + a_{nn}x_n^{k+1} &= y_n . \end{aligned} \tag{10.2}$$

If we rewrite these equations we have:

$$x_j^{k+1} = \frac{1}{a_{jj}}\Big(y_j - \sum_{l\neq j} a_{jl}x_l^k\Big) \qquad (j = 1, 2, \cdots, n).$$

We know that this scheme will converge when $N_\infty(\alpha^{-1}\beta) < 1$ (e.g. $N_\infty(\alpha^{-1}\beta) \leqslant q$ if $\Sigma_{k\neq i} \mid a_{ik} \mid \leqslant q(a_{ii})$ where $q < 1$. See (6.5) p. 16).

In case (2) the scheme is

$$\begin{aligned} a_{11}x_1^{k+1} + a_{12}x_2^k + \cdots + a_{1n}x_n^k &= y_1 \\ a_{21}x_1^{k+1} + a_{22}x_2^{k+1} + \cdots + \cdots &= y_2 \\ \cdots\cdots\cdots\cdots\cdots\cdots\cdots\cdots\cdots\cdots& \\ a_{n1}x_1^{k+1} + a_{n2}x_2^{k+1} + \cdots + a_{nn}x_n^{k+1} &= y_n \end{aligned} \tag{10.3}$$

where our matrix decomposition is now

$$\alpha = \begin{pmatrix} a_{11} & 0 & \cdots & 0 \\ a_{21} & a_{22} & \cdots & 0 \\ \cdots & \cdots & \cdots & \cdots \\ a_{n1} & a_{n2} & \cdots & a_{nn} \end{pmatrix}$$

$$\beta = \begin{pmatrix} 0 & a_{12} & \cdots & a_{1n} \\ 0 & 0 & \cdots & a_{2n} \\ \cdots & \cdots & \cdots & \cdots \\ 0 & 0 & \cdots & 0 \end{pmatrix}. \tag{10.4}$$

We have to investigate now when this scheme is convergent. We shall prove convergence whenever a is hermitian and definite. If a is not hermitian and definite it can be made so artificially by replacing the system $ax = y$ by $a^*ax = a^*y = Y$. Then a^*a is hermitian for $| a | \neq 0$. Since for $x \neq 0$, letting $a^*a = A$,

$$x^*Ax = x^*a^*ax = N_2(ax)^2 > 0,$$

A is positive definite. Letting $A = \alpha + \beta$, where α is the matrix consisting of the elements of A on and below the diagonal of A, our iteration scheme is

$$\alpha x^{k+1} = - \beta x^k + Y \tag{10.5}$$

where $Y = a^*y = Ax$. According to previous results the iteration converges if all the eigenvalues of $\alpha^{-1}\beta$ are inside the unit circle.

Now $\alpha + \beta$ is a definite hermitian matrix. $\alpha - \beta^*$ is the diagonal of $\alpha + \beta = A$. This matrix $\alpha - \beta^*$ is easily seen to be again hermitian and definite. We shall prove:

Theorem: Whenever $\alpha + \beta$ and $\alpha - \beta^*$ are positive definite hermitian matrices then the eigenvalues of $\alpha^{-1}\beta$ lie inside the unit circle.

Proof: Let λ be an eigenvalue of $\alpha^{-1}\beta$. Then there is an $x \neq 0$ such that;

$$\alpha^{-1}\beta x = \lambda x.$$

Hence

$$\beta x = \lambda \alpha x$$

$$(\alpha + \beta) x = (1 + \lambda) \alpha x = Ax.$$

Now, $\lambda \neq - 1$ since $x \neq 0$ and $\lambda = - 1$ implies $| \alpha + \beta | = | A | = 0$ which is not true. We may therefore divide by $1 + \lambda$, and find

$$\frac{x^*Ax}{1 + \lambda} = x^*\alpha x.$$

Also

$$x^*\beta^* = \bar{\lambda} x^*\alpha^* = \bar{\lambda} x^*(A - \beta^*)$$

$$= \frac{\bar{\lambda}}{1 + \bar{\lambda}} x^*A$$

$$x^*\beta^*x = \frac{\bar{\lambda}}{1 + \bar{\lambda}} x^*Ax.$$

So that

$$x^*(\alpha - \beta^*)\, x = \left[\frac{1}{1+\lambda} - \frac{\bar\lambda}{1+\bar\lambda}\right] x^*Ax$$
$$= \frac{1 - \lambda\bar\lambda}{(1+\lambda)(1+\bar\lambda)}\, x^*Ax.$$

However, $(\alpha - \beta^*)$ is positive definite and so is A. Therefore the factor of Ax is positive and real and

$$\frac{1 - \lambda\bar\lambda}{(1+\lambda)(1+\bar\lambda)} > 0$$

or

$$1 - |\lambda|^2 > 0$$

and

$$1 > |\lambda|^2 .$$

Q.E.D.

11. Accelerated Iteration Schemes

There are also some more involved iteration schemes which converge more rapidly. We had for matrices [See (7.2), p. 17];

$$c_{k+1} = c + rc_k = c + (1 - ca)\, c_k$$
$$= c_k + c(1 - ac_k).$$

If we replace c by c_k in each step we find we sharpen the iteration, for then we have, writing "1" for the unit matrix "I",

$$c_{k+1} = c_k + (c_k - c_k a c_k) = c_k + (1 - c_k a)\, c_k \qquad (11.1)$$

and letting

$$r_k = 1 - c_k a$$

we find

$$r_{k+1} = 1 - c_{k+1}a$$
$$= 1 - c_k a - c_k a + c_k a\, c_k a$$
$$= (1 - c_k a)^2 = r_k^2 . \qquad (11.2)$$

Therefore

$$r_k = r_0^{2^k}$$

and

$$a^{-1} - c_k = r_k a^{-1} = r_0^{2^k} a^{-1} . \tag{11.3}$$

This iteration will converge if some norm of r_0, say $N(r_0)$, $= q < 1$ which in turn implies [See (6.3), p. 15]

$$N(a^{-1}) < \frac{N(c_0)}{1 - q} .$$

The net error is

$$N(a^{-1} - c_k) < \frac{N(c_0)\, q^{2^k}}{1 - q} \tag{11.4}$$

which shows convergence to be much more rapid than with any of the previous schemes. Here with $2n^3k$ multiplications we get the same accuracy as with $n^3 2^k$ multiplications before. If we carry this scheme through with an inherent error, i.e.

$$c_{k+1} = c_k + (1 - c_k a)\, c_k + \epsilon,$$

we will get the bound $N(r_k) \leqslant (2q)^{2^k}$ for the error as long as $N(\epsilon)\, N(a) < q^{2^k}$. The major limitation to this scheme is that it cannot provide direct recursion formulae for vectors x^k.

We gain additional insight into the convergence if we take

$$\begin{aligned} c_k &= c_{k-1} + r_{k-1} c_{k-1} = (1 + r_{k-1})\, c_{k-1} \\ &= \left[\prod_{l=0}^{k-1} (1 + r_l)\right] c_0 \\ &= \left[\prod_{l=0}^{k-1} (1 + r_0^{2^l})\right] c_0 . \end{aligned} \tag{11.5}$$

Then

$$a^{-1} = \left[\prod_{l=0}^{\infty} (1 + r_0^{2^l})\right] c_0; \qquad r_0 = (1 - c_0 a)$$

and

$$1 = \left[\prod_{l=0}^{\infty} (1 + r_0^{2^l})\right] (1 - r_0) . \tag{11.6}$$

This formula is analogous to the well-known identity

$$(1+x)(1+x^2)(1+x^4)\cdots = \frac{1}{1-x}.$$

We can formulate schemes which converge still more rapidly by using, for example,

$$r_{k+1} = 1 - c_{k+1}a = (1 - c_k a)^3 = (r_k)^3$$

that is

$$c_{k+1} = [3 - 3c_k a + (c_k a)^2]\, c_k \tag{11.7}$$

where 11.7 is our new recursion formula. Five steps with this formula are equivalent to 3^5 steps with the earlier one. Here we chose r^3; we can consider r^4, r^5 etc. just as well.

12. Gradient Methods

There are techniques for obtaining the vector solution of $ax = y$ by minimizing various functions. These are known as gradient methods. Some of them have the advantage of converging in a finite number of steps.

We start with a function $\phi(x)$ defined by

$$\begin{aligned}\phi(x) &= N_2(y - ax)^2 \\ &= (y - ax)^* (y - ax).\end{aligned} \tag{12.0}$$

Then as a measure of the error we let $r = y - ax$. We have a solution when

$$\phi(x) = r^* r = 0.$$

If we take x as our first approximation and x^1 as a better approximation, then we relate them by

$$x^1 = x + \lambda z \tag{12.1}$$

where λ is real and both λ and z are to be suitably determined. Then

$$\begin{aligned}r^1 &= y - ax^1 = y - ax - \lambda az \\ &= r - \lambda az\end{aligned}$$

so that

$$\begin{aligned}\phi(x^1) &= (r - \lambda az)^* (r - \lambda az)\\ &= (r^* - \lambda z^*a^*) (r - \lambda az)\\ &= r^*r - \lambda(z^*a^*r + r^*az) + \lambda^2 z^*a^*az.\end{aligned}$$

This is a quadratic expression in λ. In general form it is

$$\phi(x^1) = p - 2q\lambda + s\lambda^2 \tag{12.2}$$

where $p = r^*r$, $q = \frac{1}{2}(r^*az + z^*a^*r)$ and $s = z^*a^*az$. We want to determine λ and z so as to minimize $\phi(x^1)$. By the elementary theory of maxima and minima our minimum is given by

$$\frac{d\phi(x^1)}{d\lambda} = -2q + 2s\lambda = 0.$$

Solving we obtain $\lambda = q/s$, therefore

$$\phi(x^1) = p - \frac{q^2}{s} = \phi(x) - \frac{q^2}{s}$$

and

$$\phi(x^1) = \phi(x) - \frac{[\mathrm{Re}\,(r^*az)]^2}{z^*a^*az}. \tag{12.3}$$

We shall have to make a choice of z and in choosing z we wish to maximize $[\mathrm{Re}\,(r^*az)]^2/z^*a^*az$. It is usually hopeless to try to find the exact z which will do this. We remark, however, that a $z \perp a^*r$ makes the numerator small while a z parallel to r^*a will make it large. We choose therefore $z = a^*r$ or $z^* = r^*a$. Then $q = r^*az = z^*z = r^*aa^*r = N_2(a^*r)^2$. This choice of z is called the *optimal direction*. We obtain

$$\frac{\phi(x^1)}{\phi(x)} = 1 - \frac{(z^*z)^2}{z^*a^*az\phi(x)}. \tag{12.4}$$

Now, $r = a^{*^{-1}}z$ and $r^* = z^*a^{-1}$; thus

$$\phi(x) = z^*a^{-1}a^{*-1}z = z^*(a^*a)^{-1}z$$

and (12.4) becomes

$$\frac{\phi(x^1)}{\phi(x)} = 1 - \frac{(z^*z)^2}{(z^*a^*az)(z^*(a^*a)^{-1}z)} \tag{12.5}$$

which is easily seen to be bounded away from one. Indeed

$$z^*a^*az = N_2(az)^2 \leqslant N_2(a)^2\, N_2(z)^2$$
$$z^*(a^*a)^{-1}\, z = N_2(a^{*-1}z)^2 \leqslant N_2(a^{*-1})^2\, N_2(z)^2$$
$$N_2(a^{*-1}) = N_2(a^{-1}).$$

Therefore (12.5) leads to

$$\frac{\phi(x^1)}{\phi(x)} \leqslant Q \leqslant 1 - \frac{1}{N_2(a)^2\, N_2(a^{-1})^2} \tag{12.6}$$

where

$$Q = \operatorname*{Max}_{z} \left[1 - \frac{(z^*z)^2}{(z^*a^*az)\,[z^*(a^*a)^{-1}\, z]}\right].$$

Thus $Q < 1$ and

$$\phi(x^1) \leqslant Q\phi(x). \tag{12.7}$$

Therefore x^1 yields a lower valve for ϕ under all circumstances. The rate of improvement depends upon $N_2(a)$ and $N_2(a^{-1})$. Actually

$$1 - \frac{1}{N_2(a)^2\, N_2(a^{-1})^2} = 1 - \frac{\lambda_m}{\lambda_M}$$

where λ_M and λ_m are respectively the maximum and minimum eigenvalues of a^*a. In fact it can be shown that q is

$$Q = \left(\frac{\lambda_M - \lambda_m}{\lambda_M + \lambda_m}\right)^2.$$

Obviously this scheme works best when all the eigenvalues of a^*a are close together.

Now let us consider the iteration scheme which corresponds to the above definitions for λ and z. Consider

$$x^{k+1} = x^k + \lambda_k z^k \tag{12.8}$$

x^0 arbitrary. As a measure for our error we will take

$$\begin{aligned} s^k &= a^*(y - ax^k) \\ &= a^*r^k = Y - Ax^k \end{aligned} \tag{12.9}$$

where again $Y = a^*y$ and $A = a^*a$. Then we choose for λ_k and z^k in (12.8) the expressions

$$z^k = a^*r^k = s^k = Y - Ax^k$$

and

$$\lambda_k = \frac{z^{k*}z^k}{z^{k*}a^*az^k} = \frac{z^{k*}z^k}{z^{k*}Az^k}.$$

Then

$$\phi(x^{k+1}) \leqslant Q\phi(x^k).$$

by recursion leads to,

$$\phi(x^k) \leqslant Q^k\phi(x^0).$$

Also

$$\phi(x^k) = r^{k*}r^k$$

$$r^k = y - ax^k = a(a^{-1}y - x^k)$$

$$= a(x - x^k).$$

Therefore

$$x - x^k = a^{-1}r^k$$

so that

$$N(x - x^k)^2 \leqslant N(a^{-1})^2 N(r^k)^2$$

and, since

$$N_2(r^k)^2 = \phi(x^k),$$

we have

$$N_2(x - x^k)^2 \leqslant N_2(a^{-1})^2 Q^k\phi(x^0). \tag{12.10}$$

Then, since

$$N_2(y - ax^0)^2 = \phi(x^0) \qquad \text{and} \qquad N_2(a^{-1})^2 = \frac{1}{\lambda_m}$$

where λ_m is the minimum eigenvalue of a^*a, (12.10) yields the error estimate

$$N_2(x - x^k)^2 \leqslant \frac{1}{\lambda_m} Q^k N_2(y - ax^0)^2.$$

13. Solution by Expansion in an Orthogonal System

We will now consider a method which converges in a finite number of steps. We start with $x^{k+1} = x^k + \lambda_k z^k$ where the choice of λ_k and z^k is still open. Through recursion this becomes

$$x^{k+1} = x^0 + \lambda_0 z^0 + \cdots + \lambda_k z^k.$$

If we have n equations in n unknowns our solution must in general be in a n dimensional space. Thus if we let $k + 1 = n$ and choose the z_i linearly independent, we will have for appropriate λ_i the exact solution x representable in the form

$$x = x^n = x^0 + \sum_{i=0}^{n-1} \lambda_i z^i . \tag{13.1}$$

To obtain the λ_i we could consider arbitrary independent z^i and solve the set of n equations for the n unknown λ_i. This is not appreciably simpler than the original problem. If the z^i were an orthogonal set with respect to A, that is if

$$z^{i*} a^* a z^j = z^{i*} A z^j = 0 \tag{13.2}$$

for $i \neq j$ and $z^k \neq 0$, $(k = 0, 1, \cdots, n - 1)$, then the z^i would be linearly independent. (If we assume a linear relationship $\Sigma\, \mu_i z^i = 0$ and multiply from the left by $z^{i*}A$ we have $\mu_i z^{i*} A z^i = 0$. But $z^{i*} A z^i \neq 0$ so that $\mu_i = 0$ for all i.) The calculation of the λ_i is simple. For from

$$x^k - x^0 = \sum_{i=0}^{k-1} \lambda_i z^i$$

we have by (13.1)

$$x - x^k = \sum_{j=k}^{n-1} \lambda_j z^j . \tag{13.3}$$

From $z^{k*} A(x - x^k) = \lambda_k z^{k*} A z^k$ we conclude

$$\lambda_k = \frac{z^{k*} a^* a(x - x^k)}{z^{k*} a^* a z^k}$$

$$= \frac{z^{k*} a^* (y - a x^k)}{z^{k*} a^* a z^k}$$

$$= \frac{z^{k*} s^k}{z^{k*} a^* a z^k}$$

$$\lambda_k = \frac{z^{k*}(Y - A x^k)}{z^{k*} a^* a z^k} \tag{13.4}$$

where s^k is defined as in (12.9). This value of λ_k is the optimal value corresponding to z^k as obtained from the expression (12.2) for real a, y. Furthermore each λ_k is a function only of x^k and z^k and not of any z^j or x^j with $j > k$.

For an error estimate we shall consider $r^k = a(x - x^k)$ instead of the customary $x - x^k$ since the $r^{k*}r^k$ estimate is easier to evaluate in a system orthogonal with respect to a^*a. Thus by (13.3)

$$r^{k*}r^k = \sum_{i=k}^{n-1} \bar{\lambda}_i \lambda_i z^{i*} A z^i . \tag{13.5}$$

14. Hestenes-Stiefel Conjugate Gradient Method*

This is a procedure of the type just discussed which at the same time gives a step by step method by which an orthogonal set z^k is constructed.

We will assume we have x^k, s^k and z^k and use the following recursion formulae in accordance with (13.4), (12.8), (12.9):

$$
\begin{aligned}
&\text{(a)} \qquad \lambda_k = \frac{z^{k*} s^k}{z^{k*} A z^k} \\
&\text{(b)} \qquad x^{k+1} = x^k + \lambda_k z^k \\
&\text{(c)} \qquad s^{k+1} = s^k - \lambda_k A z^k \\
&\text{(d)} \qquad \mu_k = -\frac{z^{k*} A s^{k+1}}{z^{k*} A z^k} \\
&\text{(e)} \qquad z^{k+1} = s^{k+1} + \mu_k z^k .
\end{aligned}
\tag{14.1}
$$

(The μ^k is chosen so as to satisfy the necessary condition $z^{k*} A z^{k+1} = 0$, for the z^k to form an orthogonal set). Here x^0 is arbitrary, $s^0 = Y - Ax^0$, and $z^0 = s^0$. The recursion will proceed until one of the denominators becomes zero. This will only happen if $z^k = 0$. We will show that $z^k = 0$ implies $s^k = 0$ which means we already have our exact solution $x^n = x$.

Lemma: For $i \neq j$ both

$$z^{i*} A z^j = 0 \qquad \text{and} \qquad s^{i*} s^j = 0 .$$

* See Hestenes [18], Hestenes and Stiefel [17].

Proof: We will use an induction argument.

Let $s^{i*}s^j = 0$ and $z^{i*}z^j = 0$ for $i \neq j$ and $i \leqslant k$, $j \leqslant k$. We have to show this implies $s^{i*}s^{k+1} = 0$ and $z^{i*}Az^{k+1} = 0$ for $i \leqslant k$ provided s^{k+1} and z^{k+1} are defined.

From (14.1c) and (14.1e)

$$\begin{aligned} s^{i*}s^{k+1} &= s^{i*}s^k - s^{i*}\lambda_k A z^k \\ &= s^{i*}s^k - \lambda_k(z^i - \mu_{i-1}z^{i-1})^* A z^k . \end{aligned}$$

For $i < k$ this equals zero from the hypothesis. For $i = k$,

$$s^{i*}s^{k+1} = s^{k*}s^k - \lambda_k(z^{k*}Az^k)$$

and from (14.1a)

$$= s^{k*}s^k - z^{k*}s^k$$

and, from (14.1e),

$$= -\mu_{k-1}z^{k-1*}s^k$$

and, from (14.1c) and (14.1a),

$$\begin{aligned} &= -\mu_{k-1}z^{k-1*}(s^{k-1} - \lambda_{k-1}Az^{k-1}) \\ &= -\mu_{k-1}(z^{k-1*}s^{k-1} - \lambda_{k-1}z^{k-1*}Az^{k-1}) \\ &= -\mu_{k-1}(0) = 0 . \end{aligned}$$

Incidentally, we see that

$$s^{k*}s^k = z^{k*}s^k . \tag{14.2}$$

Now, for $z^{i*}Az^{k+1}$ by (14.1e) and (14.1c) we have for $i < k$

$$\begin{aligned} z^{i*}Az^{k+1} &= z^{i*}A(s^{k+1} + \mu_k z^k) \\ &= z^{i*}As^{k+1} \\ &= (Az^i)^* s^{k+1} \\ &= \frac{1}{\lambda_i}(s^i - s^{i+1})^* s^{k+1} \\ &= 0. \end{aligned}$$

If $i = k$

$$z^{k*} A z^{k+1} = z^{k*} A(s^{k+1} + \mu_k z^k)$$
$$= 0.$$

This follows from the definition of μ_k. However, we must still make sure $\lambda_i \neq 0$ for all $i < k$. Assume $\lambda_i = 0$. This implies $z^{i*} s^i = 0$ from (14.1a). By (14.2) we would have $s^{i*} s^i = 0$. Then $s^i = 0$, or, equivalently, x^i is already the exact solution and our iteration has stopped in a previous step since $s^i = 0$ gives $\mu_{i-1} = 0$ from (14.1d) and $z^i = 0$ from (14.1e).

The lemma enables us to simplify (14.1a and d). Since $z^{k*} s^k = s^{k*} s^k$ we have

$$\lambda_k = \frac{s^{k*} s^k}{z^{k*} A z^k} > 0 . \tag{14.3a}$$

Moreover

$$\mu_k = \frac{-(Az^k)^* s^{k+1}}{z^{k*} A z^k}$$
$$= \frac{-(s^k - s^{k+1})^* s^{k+1}}{\lambda_k z^{k*} A z^k}$$
$$= \frac{s^{k+1*} s^{k+1}}{\lambda_k z^{k*} A z^k},$$

and since $\lambda_k > 0$ from (14.3a)

$$\mu_k = \frac{s^{k+1*} s^{k+1}}{s^{k*} s^k} . \tag{14.3b}$$

We still have to investigate the consequences of $z^k = 0$. Let k be the smallest value such that $z^k = 0$. Now from (14.1e)

$$z^k = 0 = s^k + \mu_{k-1} z^{k-1}$$
$$0 = s^{k-1*} s^k + \mu_{k-1} s^{k-1*} z^{k-1}$$
$$= \mu_{k-1} s^{k-1*} z^{k-1} .$$

Now $\mu_{k-1} s^{k-1*} z^{k-1} = 0$ implies either $\mu_{k-1} = 0$ and therefore by (14.3b) $s^k = a^*(y - ax^k) = 0$, or $s^{k-1} = 0$. But s^{k-1} cannot equal zero from (14.1d) and (14.1e) since k is the smallest value such that $z^k = 0$. Therefore $s^k = 0$ and we have the exact solution $x = x^k$.

15. The Elimination Method

We shall conclude our treatment of $ax = y$ with a discussion of various methods for finding the solution directly by elimination.

From its definition the determinant

$$|a| = \begin{vmatrix} a_{11} & a_{12} & \cdots & a_{in} \\ \vdots & & & \\ a_{n1} & \cdots & \cdots & a_{nn} \end{vmatrix} \tag{15.0}$$

can be written as a sum of $n!$ monomials of n factors each. Therefore, counting only multiplications as significant operations, a determinant requires $n!(n - 1)$ operations for its evaluation.

Now in employing Cramer's rule we must evaluate $n + 1$ such determinants and then perform n division, considering division as much work as multiplication. We would require $(n + 1)(n - 1)\,n! + n$ multiplications and divisions for complete solution.

There are, however, other schemes for the calculation of determinants which are usually more economical. Consider the determinant $|a|$ of (15.0) with the proviso that $a_{11} \neq 0$. (This can always be accomplished, if $|a| \neq 0$, through appropriate interchange of rows and columns.) By operations which do not change the value of $|a|$ we can obtain

$$|a| = \begin{vmatrix} a_{11} & a_{12} & \cdots & a_{1n} \\ 0 & a_{22} - \dfrac{a_{21}}{a_{11}} a_{12} & \cdots & a_{2n} - \dfrac{a_{21}}{a_{11}} a_{1n} \\ & \vdots & & \\ 0 & a_{n2} - \dfrac{a_{n1}}{a_{11}} a_{12} & \cdots & a_{nn} - \dfrac{a_{n1}}{a_{11}} a_{1n} \end{vmatrix} \tag{15.1}$$

Then, we have formed $n - 1$ quotients of the form a_{j1}/a_{11} and and we have performed $(n - 1)^2$ multiplications of the form $(a_{j1}/a_{11})\,a_{1p}$. Here, for an nth order determinant, letting $k(n)$ equal the number of operations necessary for complete evaluation, we have:

$$k(n) \leqslant [(n - 1)^2 + n - 1 + k(n - 1)] + 1. \tag{15.2}$$

If we carry the process to its conclusion, we obtain by recursion:

$$k(n) \leqslant \sum_{j=2}^{n} [j(j-1)+1] . \tag{15.3}$$

Now

$$\sum_{j=2}^{n} [j(j-1)+1] = \frac{n^3}{3} + 0(n^2)$$

so that essentially $n^3/3$ multiplications and/or divisions are necessary for evaluation.

We have already assumed multiplication and division as equal operations. We have, furthermore, neglected any other possible complications which could enter through the intrinsic characteristics of our calculating equipment. For an intelligent use of the above estimates in any particular instance all these possibilities would have to be taken into account. Counting the number of multiplications and divisions can only give a crude measure for the amount of work involved.

If we use the method of (15.1) for our determinant evaluation and then apply Cramer's rule, we find that $n^4/3 + 0(n^3)$ operations are necessary for solution.

We consider now the application of the above method directly to $ax = y$, or to the system

$$\begin{matrix} a_{11}x_1 + a_{12}x_2 + \cdots + a_{1n}x_n = y_1 \\ \vdots \qquad \vdots \qquad\qquad \vdots \quad \vdots \\ a_{n1}x_1 + a_{n2}x_2 + \cdots + a_{nn}x_n = y_n . \end{matrix} \tag{15.4}$$

Applying the elimination method of (15.1) we obtain:

$$\begin{matrix} a_{11}x_1 + a_{12}x_2 + \cdots = y_1 \\ \left(a_{22} - \frac{a_{21}}{a_{11}} a_{12}\right) x_2 + \cdots = y_2 - \frac{a_{21}}{a_{11}} y_1 \\ \vdots \qquad\qquad \vdots \\ \left(a_{n2} - \frac{a_{n1}}{a_{11}} a_{12}\right) x_2 + \cdots = y_n - \frac{a_{n1}}{a_{11}} y_1 . \end{matrix} \tag{15.5}$$

When we carry this scheme to its conclusion we have finally a system of the form

$$\begin{aligned}
b_{11}x_1 + b_{12}x_2 + \cdots \quad\quad + b_{1n}x_n &= z_1 \\
b_{22}x_2 + \cdots \quad\quad + b_{2n}x_n &= z_2 \\
&\vdots \\
b_{n-1,n-1}x_{n-1} + b_{n-1,n}x_n &= z_{n-1} \\
b_{nn}x_n &= z_n \,. \qquad (15.6)
\end{aligned}$$

This entire operation is equivalent to a series of multiplications by lower unit triangular matrices of an appropriate type.

We have a slightly different estimate for the number of operations necessary since we have an extra column, namely, the y_2. Thus the first step requires $(n - 1)$ extra operations. Therefore the total number of operations necessary to obtain (15.6) is

$$\sum_{j=2}^{n} j^2 - 1 = \frac{n^3}{3} + 0(n^2)\,.$$

Now to solve for the x_i requires $\Sigma_1^n j$ extra steps. Therefore the total number of steps required for solution is

$$\frac{n^3}{3} + \sum_{j=1}^{n} j + 0(n^2) = \frac{n^3}{3} + 0(n^2)\,.$$

We can use this method to solve for a^{-1} if we utilize n linearly independent sets of y_k. This would require $n^4/3$ operations.

The above estimates are useful primarily for comparison with the number of operations necessary for a similar degree of accuracy using iteration methods.

A complete error analysis is extremely difficult for the above method due to difficulties arising from division (e.g. if b_{jj} is small, then dividing by it increases errors) and from the possible rearrangements of the matrix.

We can make use of the following observation to obtain a bound for our error.

The kth principle minor of an nth order determinant E_k is that minor whose matrix has the diagonal $a_{11}, a_{22}, \cdots, a_{kk}$.

It is easy to see that the set of operations utilized for (15.6), in the order they are performed, constitute for any E_k only allowable determinant transformations on E_k. Thus the kth principal minor E_k of $| a |$ is given by $E_k = b_{11} \cdots b_{kk}$. Therefore $b_{kk} = E_k/E_{k-1}$ which as we have seen above should not be too small. Then $E_n = | a |$, therefore certainly $1/b_{nn} = E_{n-1}/| a |$. Now $E_{n-1}/| a |$ is one of the elements of a^{-1} and thus $1/b_{nn}$ gives a lower bound for $N_\infty(a^{-1})$ and hence for the error inherent in the solution of the system. A detailed discussion of the error in the elimination scheme will be found in v. Neumann and Goldstine [32] and Goldstine and v. Neumann [13].

CHAPTER 2

Solutions of Non-Linear Equations and Systems of Equations

1. Number of Real Zeros of a Polynomial in an Interval

We shall deal with methods for the evaluation of the roots of an equation which require that we already possess an approximate root. We therefore first discuss methods for locating roots roughly.

There are two general theories, one using real variable considerations, and the other using complex variable methods. The latter is valid only when we have analytic functions.

We shall consider the former first, as embodied in Sturm's method. This enables us to calculate the exact number of real roots a real polynomial possesses in an interval $[a, b]$*. It is particularly important to be able to do this when some of the roots are close together.

We first note that if $f(x)$ is continuous on $[a, b]$ and $f(a)\,f(b) < 0$ then there exists at least one, and in general an odd number of roots in $[a, b]$. If $f(a)\,f(b) \geqslant 0$ then all we can assert is that there are none or an even number of roots in $[a, b]$.

For Sturm's method we let $f(x)$ be our polynomial and $f_1(x) = f'(x)$. We consider a sequence of $f_i(x)$ formed in the following manner as in Euclid's algorithm:

$$
\begin{aligned}
f(x) &= g_1(x)\,f_1(x) - f_2(x)\\
f_1(x) &= g_2(x)\,f_2(x) - f_3(x)\\
&\ \vdots \\
f_l(x) &= g_{l+1}(x)\,f_{l+1}(x) - f_{l+2}(x)
\end{aligned}
\tag{1.1}
$$

* See Hochstrasser [20], Hildebrand [21], Householder [19].

where the degree of $f_{j+1}(x)$ is always greater than that of $f_{j+2}(x)$. We continue this process until no remainder occurs. We then have, say, $f_{l+1}(x) = g_{l+2}(x) f_{l+2}(x)$ and $f_{l+2}(x)$ is the greatest common divisor of $f(x)$ and $f_1(x)$. We make the further assumption that $f(a) \neq 0$; $f(b) \neq 0$; and that $f(x)$ has only simple roots in $[a, b]$. This assumption leads immediately to $f_{l+2}(x) \neq 0$ in $[a, b]$. For, otherwise, $f_1(x) = f'(x)$ would have a root in common with $f(x)$ in $[a, b]$. Then $f(x)$ would have a double root contrary to our assumption.

Moreover, no two successive $f_j(x)$, $f_{j+1}(x)$ can vanish simultaneously since this would again imply, through the defining formulae (1.1) that $f(x)$ and $f_1(x)$ have a common root. Therefore if $f_k(x_0) = 0$ then $f_{k+1}(x_0) f_{k-1}(x_0) < 0$ from the above and (1.1).

Let $w(x)$ be the number of changes in sign in going along the sequence $f(x)$, $f_1(x) \cdots, f_{l+2}(x)$, with the convention that if some $f_k = 0$ we will omit it from the sequence.

It is apparent that the only way $w(x)$ could change with x is if some f_k became zero in $[a, b]$. Let $f_k(x_0) = 0$ where $0 < k < l + 2$ and consider $f_{k-1}(x)$, $f_{k+1}(x)$. These must have opposite signs in a sufficiently small neighborhood, say $| x_0 - x | < 2\delta$; since $f_{k-1}(x_0) f_{k+1}(x_0) < 0$, neither of these will change sign. Hence the sequence $f_{k-1}(x)$, $f_k(x)$, $f_{k+1}(x)$ contributes exactly one change in sign for all x near x_0, i.e., $w(x)$ is constant near x_0. Since also $f_{l+2}(x) \neq 0$ we see that only changes in sign of $f(x)$ can contribute to changes in $w(x)$.

There are only two cases to consider when $f(\xi) = 0$; namely $f'(\xi) > 0$ in which case $f(\xi - \delta) < 0$ and $f(\xi + \delta) > 0$, or $f'(\xi) < 0$ in which case $f(\xi - \delta) > 0$ and $f(\xi + \delta) < 0$. Thus $w(\xi - \delta) - w(\xi + \delta) = 1$ in all cases. Therefore,

$$w(a) - w(b) = \text{number of zeros of } f(x) \text{ in } [a, b], \tag{1.2}$$

which is Sturm's result.

If we are not given a polynomial with only simple roots we may find one which is a factor of our original polynomial since, in the above notation,

$$\frac{f(x)}{f_{l+2}(x)}$$

has only simple roots.

2. Number of Complex Zeros of an Analytic Function inside a Curve

We shall now consider methods of utilizing complex variable theory, first noting that a polynomial is an entire analytic function which has a pole at infinity.

We may calculate the number of roots of any analytic function regular in a simply connected domain D, inside a closed rectifiable curve C in D where $f(z)$ has no zeros on C by the formula

$$N = \frac{1}{2\pi i} \oint_c \frac{f'(\zeta)}{f(\zeta)} \, d\zeta \,. \tag{2.1}$$

(If poles exist N is equal to the number of zeros less the number of poles). We may calculate N by numerical integration and if our error is less than $\frac{1}{2}$ we will have the exact number of zeros inside C. This method takes all the roots, complex and real, into account. However, it does not give the exact location of the roots.

A simple extension of formula (2.1) gives us the symmetric functions of the roots $z_1, z_2, \cdots, z_N$ inside C, from which, in principle, the roots could be found. Using the calculus of residues we have, for example:

If $N = 1$

$$z_1 = \frac{1}{2\pi i} \oint \frac{\zeta f'(\zeta)}{f(\zeta)} \, d\zeta \,.$$

If $N = 2$

$$z_1 + z_2 = \frac{1}{2\pi i} \oint \frac{\zeta f'(\zeta)}{f(\zeta)} \, d\zeta$$

and

$$z_1^2 + z_2^2 = \frac{1}{2\pi i} \oint \frac{\zeta^2 f'(\zeta)}{f(\zeta)} \, d\zeta \,.$$

This will give us $z_1 z_2 = \frac{1}{2}(z_1 + z_2)^2 - \frac{1}{2}({z_1}^2 + {z_2}^2)$, and thus z_1 and z_2 by solving a quadratic equation. This procedure may be extended in an obvious manner to $N = k$.

3. Common Roots of Two Real Functions of Two Real Variables

We shall now treat the location of common roots of a system of two equations $u(x, y)$ and $v(x, y)$. We shall first require $f = u + iv$ to be analytic. Then, as we know, the number of roots $z = x + iy$ of f inside $\mathfrak{C}$, i.e., of common solutions (x, y) of $u(x, y) = 0$, $v(x, y) = 0$ is given by

$$\frac{1}{2\pi i}\oint_{\mathfrak{C}} \frac{f'(z)}{f(z)}\, dz = N$$

where N is an integer. Therefore

$$\begin{aligned} N &= \operatorname{Re} \frac{1}{2\pi i}\oint_{\mathfrak{C}} \frac{f'(z)}{f(z)}\, dz \\ &= \operatorname{Re} \frac{1}{2\pi i}\oint_{\mathfrak{C}} d\log f(z) \\ &= \frac{1}{2\pi}\oint_{\mathfrak{C}} \operatorname{Re} \frac{1}{i}\, d\log f(z) \\ &= \frac{1}{2\pi}\oint_{\mathfrak{C}} d\,(\operatorname{Im.} \log f(z)) \\ &= \frac{1}{2\pi}\oint_{\mathfrak{C}} d\phi \end{aligned} \tag{3.1}$$

where if

$$f(z) = u(x, y) + iv(x, y) \qquad \text{and} \qquad z = x + iy$$

then

$$\phi = \arc\tan \frac{v}{u} = \operatorname{Im.} \log f(z).$$

or more precisely:

$$\cos\phi = \frac{u}{\sqrt{u^2 + v^2}},$$

$$\sin\phi = \frac{v}{\sqrt{u^2 + v^2}}.$$

Thus we see that if we attach to each point (x, y) in the xy plane the vector (u, v) then ϕ is the angle between (u, v) and the positive x axis. Obviously, ϕ is determined within $2\pi p$, p an integer; different values of p ensuing according to the procedure we adopt in assigning ϕ to (u, v). Let u and v be continuous. Thus the vector field is continuous and we can continue ϕ along the curve. Let us take a point (x_0, y_0) and assign to it $\phi_0 + 2n_0\pi$, n_0 a constant integer and then go around the curve once in a positive sense. We obtain a new ϕ at (x_0, y_0) say $\phi_0 + 2\pi n$. Now since we have chosen our curve $\mathcal{C}$ to be free of zeros and poles we have:

$$N = \frac{1}{2\pi}\oint d\phi = \frac{1}{2\pi}[\phi_0 + 2\pi n - \phi_0 - 2\pi n_0]$$

$$= n - n_0 .$$

It is easily seen that $n - n_0$ is the number of times (u, v) makes a complete positive revolution minus the number of negative revolutions while going around the curve in a positive sense.

Let us consider one such curve $\mathcal{C}$ with parametric representation $x = x(t)$; $y = y(t)$; $0 \leqslant t \leqslant 1$. From

$$\phi = \arctan\frac{v}{u} + n\pi$$

we have

$$d\phi = \frac{udv - vdu}{u^2 + v^2} .$$

If ϕ changes differentiably with t we have:

$$\frac{1}{2\pi}\oint_{\mathcal{C}} d\phi = \frac{1}{2\pi}\oint_{\mathcal{C}} \frac{d\phi}{dt}\, dt .$$

Moreover, if we consider our expression for $d\phi$ along the curve we have:

$$\frac{1}{2\pi}\oint_{\mathcal{C}} \frac{d\phi}{dt}\, dt = \int_0^1 \frac{u\left(\frac{dv}{dx}\frac{dx}{dt} + \frac{dv}{dy}\frac{dy}{dt}\right) - v\left(\frac{du}{dx}\frac{dx}{dt} + \frac{du}{dy}\frac{dy}{dt}\right)}{u^2 + v^2}\, dt. \qquad (3.2)$$

Formula (3.2) for ϕ may be expressed, as any integral, as $(1/2\pi)\,\Sigma\,(\phi_{k+1} - \phi_k)$ which again gives the number of times, direction of rotation taken into account, which ϕ turns around the curve. We may visualize this by considering the vector (u, v) as having a fixed initial point and rotating as (u, v) moves on the curve.

The evaluation of $\lim_{k\to\infty} \Sigma\,(\phi_{k-1} - \phi_k)$ may, in the case where (u, v) does not vary too radically along the arcs $t_k < t < t_{k+1}$ of $\mathscr{C}$, be reduced to a finite sum since all we require is that we miss no complete revolution or equivalently (u, v) does not make a complete revolution while ϕ varies from ϕ_k to ϕ_{k+1}:

$$\left| \int_{t_k}^{t} \frac{d\phi}{dt}\, dt \right| < \pi \qquad \text{for} \quad t_k < t < t_{k+1}\,.$$

It remains to find an interpretation for $1/2\pi \oint_{\mathscr{C}} d\phi$ when $f = u + iv$ is not necessarily analytic. First of all:

$$\frac{1}{2\pi} \oint_{\mathscr{C}} d\phi = N$$

is necessarily an integer. Let us consider the effect of deforming $\mathscr{C}$ continuously such that no common zero of v and u is passed through or, equivalently, $u^2 + v^2 \neq 0$. Let dy/dt and dx/dt vary continuously also. Let us introduce a parameter λ such that $\mathscr{C}_\lambda$ has equations $x = x(t, \lambda)$; $y = y(t, \lambda)$; $0 \leqslant t \leqslant 1$. In the integral (3.2) will depend continuously on λ if the numerator and the denominator do and the denominator is not equal to zero. Then this integral has an integer as its value and it changes continuously; it cannot "jump" an integral amount in value or, equivalently, it must remain constant.

If no common zero of u, v is in the inside, $\mathscr{C}_\lambda$ may be contracted to an arbitrarily small curve, say, $\mathscr{C}_0$. Then ϕ varies very little along $\mathscr{C}_0$ and therefore must return to its original value since it cannot vary by as much as 2π in this case. Therefore:

$$\frac{1}{2\pi} \oint_{\mathscr{C}} d\phi = \frac{1}{2\pi} \oint_{\mathscr{C}_0} d\phi = 0$$

where no common zero of u and v lies inside $\mathscr{C}$.

If, on the other hand, there is a common zero of u and v inside $\mathscr{C}$ then we make use of the additivity of line integrals: If the region bounded by the oriented closed curve $\mathfrak{C}$ is decomposed into regions bounded by the similarly oriented closed curves $\mathfrak{C}_1$ and $\mathfrak{C}_2$ we have

$$\oint_{\mathfrak{C}} d\phi = \oint_{\mathfrak{C}_1} d\phi + \oint_{\mathfrak{C}} d\phi$$

or

$$N_{\mathfrak{C}} = N_{\mathfrak{C}_1} + N_{\mathfrak{C}_2} .$$

This suggests that the value around any arbitrary curve $\mathfrak{C}$ on which u and v do not have a common zero or pole can be equated to the sum of values of N around small circles, say, with center at the common zeros of u and v inside $\mathfrak{C}$.

We also have the following theorem which is analogous to Rouché's theorem for complex functions.

Theorem: Given a vector field (u, v) and $u = u_1 + u_2$; $v = v_1 + v_2$ such that $u_1{}^2 + v_1{}^2 > u_2{}^2 + v_2{}^2$ along $\mathfrak{C}$. Then

$$N_c(u, v) = N_c(u_1 , v_1) .$$

Proof: We need that for any λ with $0 \leqslant \lambda \leqslant 1$

$$(u_1 + \lambda u_2)^2 + (v_1 + \lambda v_2)^2 > 0;$$

[otherwise

$$u_1 + \lambda u_2 = 0, \qquad v_1 + \lambda v_2 = 0$$

$$u_1^2 + v_1^2 = \lambda^2(u_2^2 + v_2^2)$$

$$\leqslant u_2^2 + v_2^2].$$

Since ϕ then depends continuously on λ, the value of

$$N_{\mathfrak{C}}(u_1 + \lambda u_2 , v_1 + \lambda v_2)$$

must be constant for $0 \leqslant \lambda \leqslant 1$ which proves the theorem.

Consider u, v and a common zero inside $\mathfrak{C}$, say at $x = 0$, $y = 0$ for simplicity (in any event a coordinate transformation can bring it there). Let:

$$u = ax + by + M\theta_1(x^2 + y^2) \qquad |\theta_1| < 1$$

$$v = cx + dy + M\theta_2(x^2 + y^2) \qquad |\theta_2| < 1 .$$

For a curve sufficiently close to (0, 0)

$$(ax + by)^2 + (cx + dy)^2 > (\theta_1^2 + \theta_2^2)\, M^2(x^2 + y^2)^2$$

if $ax + by$ and $cx + dy$ cannot become zero simultaneously or, equivalently, $ad - bc \neq 0$, that is $u_x v_y - u_y v_x \neq 0$ at the common zero.

It is therefore sufficient for the determination of N_c to use linear functions or linear vector fields.

Then $ax + by$ and $cx + dy$ and, therefore, $\oint_{\mathscr{C}} d\phi$ depend continuously on a, b, c, and d. Thus $N_c(ax + by, cx - dy)$ depends continuously on a, b, c and d along a simple closed curve $\mathscr{C}$ about (0, 0) as long as $ad - bc \neq 0$.

Since the set of matrices with positive [negative] determinants is connected we find: if $\det \begin{pmatrix} a & b \\ c & d \end{pmatrix} > 0$ [$\det \begin{pmatrix} a & b \\ c & d \end{pmatrix} < 0$] then $\begin{pmatrix} a & b \\ c & d \end{pmatrix}$ can be continuously transformed into $\begin{pmatrix} 1 & 0 \\ 0 & 1 \end{pmatrix}$ [$\begin{pmatrix} 1 & 0 \\ 0 & -1 \end{pmatrix}$] in the set.

Obviously, $N_c(x, y) = 1$; $N_c(x, -y) = -1$. Therefore:

$$\frac{1}{2\pi} \oint_{\mathscr{C}} d\phi = N_{\mathscr{C}} = \sum \operatorname{sign}\,(u_x v_y - u_y v_x) \tag{3.3}$$

where sign $(u_x v_y - u_y v_x)$ is taken at every common zero of u and v inside $\mathscr{C}$ and where we restrict ourselves to fields in which $u_x v_y - u_y v_x$ do not vanish for common zeros.

If we go back to our vector with a fixed initial point, say (0, 0), we observe that this vector will complete, in general, several revolutions.

If we consider the number of times the vector crosses the x-axis we have:

$N_{\mathscr{C}}$ = number of times the vector crosses the positive [negative] x-axis in a positive sense minus the number of times in a negative sense. Therefore

$N_{\mathscr{C}}$ = (number of zeros of v when $u > 0$ and v goes from $-$ to $+$) $-$ (number of zeros of v when $u > 0$ and v goes from $+$ to $-$)

= (number of zeros of v when $u < 0$ and v goes from $+$ to $-$) $-$ (number of zeros of v when $u < 0$ and v goes from $-$ to $+$).

Let $p[q]$* equal the number of zeros of v on $\mathscr{C}$ in passing through which uv becomes > 0 [uv becomes < 0]. Then $N_{\mathscr{C}} = (p - q)/2$.

4. Number of Common Zeros of Two Real Polynomials of x, y Inside a Polygon

Consider a polygon $\mathscr{C}$ with one specific side $\overrightarrow{XY}$ given by $x = at + b$, $y = ct + d$; $0 \leqslant t \leqslant 1$. Let t increasing indicate a positive sense of rotation. If u and v are polynomials then u and v along $\overrightarrow{XY}$ are given by real polynomials in t: $u(t)$ and $v(t)$.

We again utilize Euclid's Algorithm as follows:

$$\begin{aligned} v(t) &= g_1(t)\, u(t) - f_1(t) \\ u(t) &= g_2(t) f_1(t) - f_2(t) \\ &\vdots \\ f_l(t) &= g_{l+2}(t) f_{l+1}(t) - f_{l+2}(t) \\ f_{l+1}(t) &= g_{l+3}(t) f_{l+2}(t)\,. \end{aligned}$$

Then $f_{j+2}(t) \neq 0$ on $\overrightarrow{XY}$ since u and v cannot have common zeros and by a similar reasoning to that used for Sturm's method we have: only changes of sign of v change the number $w(t)$ of changes of sign in $v, u, f_1, \cdots, f_{l+2}$. Then for $v(t) = 0$

$$w(t + 0) = w(t - 0) - 1 \quad \text{if} \quad u, v \text{ change from opposite signs to like signs}$$

$$w(t + 0) = w(t - 0) + 1 \quad \text{if} \quad u, v \text{ change from like signs to opposite signs.}$$

Therefore the contributions to $p - q$ from $\overrightarrow{XY}$ is $w(X) - w(Y)$ where $X = (b, d)$ and $Y = (a + b, c + d)$. We can do this for all sides of our polygon and compute $N_{\mathscr{C}}$.

* Bracket indicates alternative propositions.

5. Zeros of a Polynomial in the Complex Half-Plane

We now wish to compute the number of zeros of a complex polynomial $f(z)$ in a half plane bounded by the straight line L given by $x = at + b$, $y = ct + d$. Then for this line

$$\left(\frac{p-q}{2}\right)_L = \frac{w(-\infty) - w(+\infty)}{2}.$$

Let a large circle be drawn with L as a diameter. We want the contributions to $(p - q)/2$ for half this circle. We note that for any $f_k(t)$ on this circle its sign will be determined by the sign of the coefficient of the highest order term in $f_k(t)$.

We consider the special case $u = \operatorname{Re} F(z)$ and $v = \operatorname{Im} f(z)$ where $f(z)$ is a polynomial in $z = x + iy$ of degree n,

$$f(z) = z^n + a_1 z^{n-1} + \cdots + a_n .$$

For large $|z|$ we have $f(z) \sim z^n$; for $z = re^{i\theta}$ then $(u, v) \sim r^n (\cos n\theta, \sin n\theta)$. Now this (u, v) goes around the circle positively only; therefore $q = 0$. Moreover,

$$p = (\text{number of crossings of positive } u \text{ axis})$$
$$+ (\text{number of crossings of negative } u \text{ axis}) .$$

Obviously, $p = 2n$ for the whole circle.

Then, since if $\operatorname{Im}(z^n) = 0$ then $\operatorname{Im}(-z)^n = 0$, we have the number of crossings on one half of the circle equal to the number of crossings on the other half. Thus $p = n$ on one half the circle. Therefore $p - q = n$ for the large half circle and:

$$\text{Number of zero in the whole half plane} = \left[\frac{w(-\infty) - w(+\infty)}{2}\right]_L + \frac{n}{2}$$

for a complex polynomial of one variable of degree n. This reduces the determination of the number of zeros of a polynomial $f(z)$ in a half plane to Euclid's Algorithm applied to its real and complex parts on the boundary.

6. Bernouilli's Method for Finding the Largest Root of an Equation

We shall now discuss several methods for the exact determination of roots of a polynomial.

The first method we consider is that of Bernoulli. We assume that we are given a homogeneous *difference equation*

$$\sum_{j=0}^{n} a_j E^j f(x) = 0 \tag{6.1}$$

with constant coefficients a_j, where E is the operator defined by $Ef(x) = f(x+1)$ so that $E^j f(x) = f(x+j)$. Then a particular solution of this difference equation is $f(x) = \lambda^x$ if λ is a root of the *characteristic equation* $\sum_j a_j \lambda^j = 0$ of the given difference equation and x is an integer. If the characteristic equation has n distinct roots $\lambda_1, \lambda_2, \cdots \lambda_n$ we shall show that

$$f(x) = \sum_{i=1}^{n} c_i \lambda_i^x,$$

where x is a positive integer, is the general solution. The general solution is obviously determined by its initial values $f(0), f(1), \cdots, f(n-1)$ at least if we assume $a_n \neq 0$. Obviously

$$f(x) = \sum_{i=1}^{n} c_l \lambda_l^x$$

represents the general solution if for any $f(0), f(1), \cdots, f(n-1)$ we can determine constants c_l such that

$$f(0) = \sum_{l=1}^{n} c_l; \qquad f(1) = \sum_{l=1}^{n} c_l \lambda_l; \qquad \cdots; \qquad f(n-1) = \sum_{l=1}^{n} c_l \lambda_l^{n-1}.$$

The determinant of this system of equations for c_l is

$$\begin{vmatrix} 1 & 1 & \cdots & 1 \\ \lambda_1 & \lambda_2 & \cdots & \lambda_n \\ \lambda_1^2 & \lambda_2^2 & \cdots & \lambda_n^2 \\ \cdots & \cdots & \cdots & \cdots \\ \lambda_1^{n-1} & \lambda_2^{n-1} & & \lambda_n^{n-1} \end{vmatrix} = \prod_{i>j} (\lambda_i - \lambda_j)$$

This determinant will be different from zero if all the λ_i are distinct.

Let us reverse the above procedure in that, given a polynomial

$$P(\lambda) = \sum_{i=0}^{n} a_i \lambda^i$$

with $a_n \neq 0$, we form and investigate the difference equation $P(E) f(x) = 0$.

We can easily obtain numerical values for $f(x)$ starting with any initial values. Assume $|\lambda_k| \leqslant q |\lambda_1|$ for $k > 1$ where $q < 1$. Then we have:

$$f(x) = c_1 \lambda_1^x + 0(|q\lambda_1|^x) \qquad \text{for} \qquad x \text{ large}$$

Thus

$$f(x) = \lambda_1^x [c_1 - 0(|q|^x)] \,.$$

Therefore

$$\frac{f(x+1)}{f(x)} = \frac{\lambda_1^{x+1}[c_1 + 0(|q|^{x+1})]}{\lambda_1^x [c_1 + 0(|q|^x)]}$$

and we obtain for the root λ_1 the formula

$$\operatorname*{Lim}_{x \to \infty} \frac{f(x+1)}{f(x)} = \lambda_1 \qquad \text{provided} \qquad c_1 \neq 0.$$

We need a condition to determine whether or not c_1 vanishes. If $c_1 = 0$ then we would have

$$f(x) = \sum_{l=2}^{n} c_j \lambda_i^x$$

and $f(x)$ would satisfy the difference equation

$$\left[\frac{P(E)}{E - \lambda_1}\right] f(x) = 0$$

Here

$$\left[\frac{P(E)}{E - \lambda_1}\right] f(x) = b_0 f(x) + b_1 f(x+1) + \cdots + b_{n-1} f(x+n-1) \,.$$

Now consider $n - 1$ more such equations obtained by replacing x by $x + 1$, $x + 2$, $\cdots$, $x + n - 1$. We then have a system of n homogeneous equations in unknowns for which we have a nontrivial solution. Therefore

$$\begin{vmatrix} f(x) & \cdots & f(x+n-1) \\ f(x+1) & \cdots & f(x+n) \\ \vdots & & \\ f(x+n-1) & \cdots & f(x+2n-2) \end{vmatrix} = 0 \qquad \text{for all} \qquad x \, .$$

We may check for $x = 0$ in which case all entries in the determinant are easily obtained from the initial values of the difference equation. Indeed no c_l vanishes if the determinant is not zero.

The above discussion assumes that no errors have been introduced. We shall investigate now what effect errors of computation will have.

Let us consider first $P(\lambda) = \lambda - \lambda_1$. Then we should have in the errorless situation $f(x + 1) - f(x) \lambda_1 = 0$. We have instead $f(x + 1) - f(x) \lambda_1 = \epsilon(x)$. Let us consider the simplest case when we take the error to have a constant value ϵ, that is when $f(x + 1) - f(x) \lambda_1 = \epsilon$. This is an inhomogeneous difference equation and requires for its solution a solution of the homogeneous equation

$$f(x+1) - f(x)\lambda_1 = 0$$

plus a particular solution of the inhomogeneous equation. Thus we have if $\lambda_1 \neq 1$

$$f(x) = c_1 \lambda_1^x + \frac{\epsilon}{1 - \lambda_1} \, .$$

Since $f(0)$ is known we have,

$$c_1 = f(0) - \left(\frac{\epsilon}{1 - \lambda_1}\right) .$$

Therefore

$$f(x) = \left[f(0) - \left(\frac{\epsilon}{1 - \lambda_1}\right)\right] \lambda_1^x + \frac{\epsilon}{1 - \lambda_1}$$

and

$$\frac{f(x+1)}{f(x)} = \frac{\left(f(0) - \dfrac{\epsilon}{1-\lambda_1}\right)\lambda_1^{x+1} + \dfrac{\epsilon}{1-\lambda_1}}{\left(f(0) - \dfrac{\epsilon}{1-\lambda_1}\right)\lambda_1^{x} + \dfrac{\epsilon}{1-\lambda_1}}.$$

Then

$$\lim_{x\to\infty}\frac{f(x+1)}{f(x)} = 1 \qquad \text{for} \qquad |\lambda_1| < 1$$

$$= 1 \qquad \text{for} \qquad f(0) - \frac{\epsilon}{1-\lambda_1} = 0$$

$$= \lambda_1 \qquad \text{if} \qquad |\lambda_1| > 1 \quad \text{and} \quad f(0) \neq \frac{\epsilon}{1-\lambda_1}.$$

This indicates that only if $|\lambda_1| > 1$ is it true that

$$\lim_{x\to\infty}\frac{f(x+1)}{f(x)}$$

converges to λ_1. For $|\lambda_1| < 1$ if we do not take $|x|$ too large we still obtain some meaningful value for λ_1 if ϵ is small enough.

However, if we require that the *relative* error is uniformly bounded, $|\epsilon(x)/f(x)| \leqslant \epsilon$, we do not need the restriction $|\lambda_1| > 1$. For if $|\epsilon(x)/f(x)| \leqslant \epsilon$ then

$$f(x+1) = \lambda_1 f(x) + \theta\epsilon \ f(x)|$$

where $|\theta| < 1$. Thus

$$\left|\frac{f(x+1)}{f(x)} - \lambda_1\right| \leqslant \epsilon.$$

A similar situation prevails in the case of the general equation. Bernouilli's method can be unstable if one only requires that the absolute computational error is small. It becomes stabile, however, if the error relative to $f(x)$ is to be small.

This method will also give the smallest root of $f(x) = 0$ in the event we take the "reciprocal" equation $x^n f(1/x) = 0$.

7. Finding the Second Largest Root

It is possible to find the second root of $P(\lambda) = 0$ utilizing the above method. We assume $\lambda_1 \neq \lambda_2$; $|\lambda_1| \geqslant |\lambda_2|$; $|\lambda_2| > |\lambda_k|$, $(k = 3 \cdots n)$ or $|\lambda_k| \leqslant q\,|\lambda_2| \leqslant q\,|\lambda_1|$ with $q < 1$ and $k > 2$.

We write the solution for the difference equation $P(E)\,f(x) = 0$ as

$$f(x) = [c_1\lambda_1^x + c_2\lambda_2^x] + \left[\sum_{j=3}^{n} c_j\lambda_j^x\right]$$

$$= g(x) + h(x)\,.$$

An estimate for $h(x)$ is $0(|\,q\lambda_2\,|^x)$. If

$$Q(E) = E^2 - (\lambda_1 + \lambda_2)\,E + \lambda_1\lambda_2$$

then

$$Q(E)\,g(x) = 0\,.$$

We shall utilize this together with the fact that $f(x)$ differs from $g(x)$ by a term of order $|\,q\lambda_2\,|^x$.

Let us write out $Q(E)\,g(x)$ for two values of x, e.g.

$$g(x+2) - (\lambda_1 + \lambda_2)\,g(x+1) + \lambda_1\lambda_2 g(x) = 0$$

$$g(x+3) - (\lambda_1 + \lambda_2)\,g(x+2) + \lambda_1\lambda_2 g(x+1) = 0\,.$$

We can now solve these two equations for $\lambda_1 + \lambda_2$ and $\lambda_1\lambda_2$.

$$\lambda_1 + \lambda_2 = \frac{\begin{vmatrix} E^2g & g \\ E^3g & Eg \end{vmatrix}}{\begin{vmatrix} Eg & g \\ E^2g & Eg \end{vmatrix}} \tag{7.1}$$

$$\lambda_1\lambda_2 = \frac{\begin{vmatrix} E^2g & Eg \\ E^3g & E^2g \end{vmatrix}}{\begin{vmatrix} Eg & g \\ E^2g & Eg \end{vmatrix}}\,. \tag{7.2}$$

Let

$$\begin{vmatrix} Eg & g \\ E^2g & Eg \end{vmatrix} = W(x)\,.$$

Then

$$W(x+1) = \lambda_1\lambda_2 W(x)$$

and, as is easily seen,

$$W(x+1) = \lambda_1^{x+1}\lambda_2^{x+1} W(0) .$$

Now we have

$$W(0) = \begin{vmatrix} g(1) & g(0) \\ g(2) & g(1) \end{vmatrix} = - c_1 c_2 (\lambda_1 - \lambda_2)^2$$

and therefore $W(0) \neq 0$ if c_1 and $c_2 \neq 0$ and $\lambda_1 \neq \lambda_2$. Hence

$$\begin{vmatrix} Ef & f \\ E^2f & Ef \end{vmatrix} = \begin{vmatrix} Eg + 0((q\lambda_2)^x) & g + 0((q\lambda_2)^x) \\ E^2g + 0((q\lambda_2)^x) & Eg + 0((q\lambda_2)^x) \end{vmatrix}$$

$$= W(x) + 0((q\lambda_1\lambda_2)^x)$$

$$= \lambda_1^x\lambda_2^x[W(0) + 0(q^x)] .$$

Therefore, if $W(0) \neq 0$,

$$\frac{\begin{vmatrix} E^2f & Ef \\ E^3f & E^2f \end{vmatrix}}{\begin{vmatrix} Ef & f \\ E^2f & Ef \end{vmatrix}} = \lambda_1\lambda_2[1 + 0(q^x)] \to \lambda_1\lambda_2 . \tag{7.3}$$

If $|\lambda_1| > |\lambda_2|$ we can obtain λ_1 as above and then compute λ_2 from $\lambda_1\lambda_2$. If $|\lambda_1| = |\lambda_2|$ and $\lambda_1 \neq \lambda_2$ or $|\lambda_1|$ is close to $|\lambda_2|$ then we solve for $\lambda_1 + \lambda_2$,

$$\lambda_1 + \lambda_2 = \frac{\begin{vmatrix} E^2g & g \\ E^3g & Eg \end{vmatrix}}{\begin{vmatrix} Eg & g \\ E^2g & Eg \end{vmatrix}}$$

and thus

$$\begin{vmatrix} E^2g & g \\ E^3g & Eg \end{vmatrix} = (\lambda_1 + \lambda_2)\,\lambda_1^x\lambda_2^x W(0) .$$

In a manner entirely analogous to that used above

$$\frac{\begin{vmatrix} E^2f & f \\ E^3f & Ef \end{vmatrix}}{\begin{vmatrix} Ef & f \\ E^2f & Ef \end{vmatrix}} = (\lambda_1 + \lambda_2)\,[1 + 0(q^x)] \to \lambda_1 + \lambda_2 \,. \tag{7.4}$$

We then have a quadratic system of equations to solve to obtain the roots. The same method has an obvious extension to the solution for the first three roots, etc.

8. Determination of the Smallest Root of an Analytic Function

We consider now an analytic function $f(z) = a_0 + a_1 z + \cdots$ with zeros $z_1, z_2, \cdots$ and $0 < |z_1| < |z_2| < \cdots < |z_n| < \cdots$. Thus $1/|z_1|$ is the radius of convergence for the series for $1/f(z)$. This radius can also be found exactly by the ratio test when $1/f(z)$ has a pole $1/z_1$ nearest to the origin as we shall see. Let

$$g(z) = \gamma_0 + \gamma_1 z + \gamma_2 z^2 + \cdots$$

be a given regular analytic function; then

$$\frac{g(z)}{f(z)} = b_0 + b_1 z + b_2 z^2 + \cdots$$

and

$$g(z) = f(z)\,\frac{g(z)}{f(z)} = \sum_{k=0}^{\infty} a_k z^k \sum_{j=0}^{\infty} b_j z^j = \sum_{n=0}^{\infty} \gamma_n z^n \,.$$

Therefore the b_k can be computed successively from the recursion formulas

$$\gamma_n = \sum_{k=0}^{n} a_{n-k} b_k \,.$$

Now,

$$\frac{g(z)}{f(z)} = \frac{g(z_1)}{f'(z_1)\,(z - z_1)} + \sum \alpha_n z^n$$

where $g(z_1)/[f'(z_1)(z - z_1)]$ is the singular part at the first pole and $\sum \alpha_n z^n$ is convergent in a larger circle. Then for $|z| < |z_1|$

$$\frac{g(z)}{f(z)} = \sum_n \left[\frac{-g(z_1)}{z_1 f'(z_1)} \left(\frac{z}{z_1}\right)^n + \alpha_n z^n \right].$$

Thus

$$b_n = -\frac{g(z_1)}{z_1 f'(z_1)} \frac{1}{(z_1)^n} + 0\left(\left(\frac{q}{z_1}\right)^n\right).$$

[The power series for the remainder still converges if z is bounded by z_1 where $|z_1/z_2| = q < 1$.] Then it follows as in the Bernouilli method with $\lambda_1 = 1/z_1$ that

$$\frac{b_{n+1}}{b_n} \to \frac{1}{z_1}.$$

Again in a way similar to that above we may consider the first and second poles of $f(z)$ in which case

$$b_n = \frac{-g(z_1)}{z_1 f'(z_1)} \frac{1}{z_1^n} - \frac{g(z_2)}{z_2 f'(z_2)} \frac{1}{z_2^n} + 0\left(\left(\frac{q}{z_2}\right)^n\right).$$

Then using the argument for Bernouilli's method [See (7.3)]

$$\frac{1}{z_1 z_2} = \lim_{n\to\infty} \frac{\begin{vmatrix} b_{n+2} & b_{n+1} \\ b_{n+3} & b_{n+2} \end{vmatrix}}{\begin{vmatrix} b_{n+1} & b_n \\ b_{n+2} & b_{n+1} \end{vmatrix}}.$$

If $f(z)$ and $g(z)$ are polynomials then the above method reduces to Bernouilli's method.

9. Graeffe Root-Squaring Process

Given

$$P(\lambda) = \sum_{k=0}^{n} a_k \lambda^k;$$

$a_n \neq 0$ we can write

$$P(\lambda) = a_n \prod_{k=1}^{n} (\lambda - \lambda_k)$$

where λ_k are the roots of the polynomial. Now the coefficients of $P(\lambda)$ are symmetric functions of the roots of $P(\lambda)$. If we were to consider the polynomial whose roots were λ_k^2 then its coefficients would be symmetric expressions of its roots and thus expressible in terms of the coefficients of $P(\lambda)$. Indeed,

$$P_1(\lambda) = (-1)^n P(\sqrt{\lambda})\, P(-\sqrt{\lambda}) = a_n^2 \prod_{k=1}^{n} (\sqrt{\lambda} - \lambda_k)\,(\sqrt{\lambda} + \lambda_k)$$

$$= a_n^2 \prod_{k=1}^{n} (\lambda - \lambda_k^2)\,. \tag{9.1}$$

is a polynomial in λ with roots λ_k^2. We note

$$P_1(\lambda) = \sum_{l=0}^{n} a_l^1 \lambda^l = (-1)^n \sum_{k=0}^{n} a_k (\sqrt{\lambda})^k \sum_{i=0}^{n} (-1)^1 a_i (\sqrt{\lambda})^i$$

$$= (-1)^n (a_0 + a_1 \sqrt{\lambda} + a_2 (\sqrt{\lambda})^2 + \cdots)$$
$$\times (a_0 - a_1 \sqrt{\lambda} + a_2 (\sqrt{\lambda})^2 - \cdots).$$

Thus the coefficients of $P_1(\lambda)$ are given by:

$$(-1)^n a_0^1 = a_0 a_0$$
$$(-1)^n a_1^1 = a_0 a_2 - a_1 a_1 + a_2 a_0$$
$$(-1)^n a_2^1 = a_0 a_4 - a_1 a_3 + a_2 a_2 - a_3 a_1 + a_4 a_0\,.$$

We shall use the root squaring procedure iteratively and define $P_0(\lambda) = P(\lambda)$, and

$$P_k(\lambda) = a_n^{2^k} \sum_{l=1}^{n} (\lambda - \lambda_l^{2^k})\,.$$

Then our iteration will have the form

$$P_{k+1}(\lambda) = (-1)^n P_k(\sqrt{\lambda})\, P_k(-\sqrt{\lambda})$$
$$= a_0^{k+1} + a_1^{k+1}\lambda + \cdots + a_{n-1}^{k+1}\lambda^{n-1} + a_n^{k+1}\lambda^n.$$

From the above definition and equation we have

$$(a_n^k) = (a_n)^{2^k} \tag{9.1}$$

$$a_{n-1}^k = -(a_n)^{2^k} \sum_{l=1}^{n} \lambda_l^{2^k} \tag{9.2}$$

$$a_{n-2}^k = (a_n)^{2^k} \sum_{i<j} \lambda_i^{2^k} \lambda_j^{2^k} . \tag{9.3}$$

Thus

$$-\frac{a_{n-1}^k}{a_n^k} = \sum_{l=1}^{n} \lambda_l^{2^k} . \tag{9.4}$$

If we assume all the roots are distinct and, say,

$$|\lambda_1| > |\lambda_2| > |\lambda_3| > \cdots > |\lambda_n|$$

then we can obtain

$$-\frac{a_{n-1}^k}{a_n^k} = \lambda_1^{2^k}\left[1 + 0\left(\left(\frac{\lambda_2}{\lambda_1}\right)^{2^k}\right)\right].$$

Thus

$$\lim_{k\to\infty} \sqrt[2^k]{-\frac{a_{n-1}^k}{a_n^k}} = \lambda_1 .$$

Clearly a very high degree of accuracy is obtainable. Moreover

$$\sqrt[2^k]{-\frac{a_{n-2}^k}{a_{n-1}^k}} = \sqrt[2^k]{\frac{\lambda_1^{2^k}\lambda_2^{2^k} + \lambda_1^{2^k}\lambda_3^{2^k} + \lambda_2^{2^k}\lambda_3^{2^k} + \cdots}{\lambda_1^{2^k} + \lambda_2^{2^k} + \cdots}}$$

$$= \lambda_2 \sqrt[2^k]{\frac{1 + 0\left[\left(\frac{\lambda_3}{\lambda_2}\right)^{2^k} + \left(\frac{\lambda_3}{\lambda_1}\right)^{2^k}\right]}{1 + \left(\frac{\lambda_2}{\lambda_1}\right)^{2^k} + \cdots}}$$

$$= \lambda_2\left(1 + 0\left[\left(\frac{\lambda_3}{\lambda_2}\right)^{2^k} + \left(\frac{\lambda_2}{\lambda_1}\right)^{2^k} + \left(\frac{\lambda_3}{\lambda_1}\right)^{2^k}\right] \to \lambda_2$$

as $k \to \infty$. Similarly

$$\sqrt[2^k]{-\frac{a_{n-3}^k}{a_{n-2}^k}} \to \lambda_3 \qquad \text{etc.}$$

10. Roots as Limits of Rational Expressions. Lehmer Method

The practical disadvantage in the above method is the difficulty of root extraction.

A method of obtaining linear relations for the roots utilizing a procedure similar to that of root squaring has been developed by Lehmer from a suggestion by Brodetsky and Smeal.* This method considers a family of polynomials dependent upon a parameter h. We define

$$Q_k(\lambda, h) = a_n^{2^k} \prod_{l=1}^{n} (\lambda - [\lambda_l + h]^{2^k}) . \tag{10.1}$$

Then [See (9.1)]

$$Q_k(\lambda, 0) = P_k(\lambda)$$

and we form

$$Q_{k+1}(\lambda, h) = (-1)^n Q_k(\sqrt{\lambda}, h)\, Q_k(-\sqrt{\lambda}, h) .$$

Now let

$$\begin{aligned} \left.\frac{\partial Q_k(\lambda, h)}{\partial h}\right|_{h=0} &= R_k(\lambda) \\ &= Q_k(\lambda, 0) \sum_{l=1}^{n} \frac{-2^k(\lambda_l)^{2^k-1}}{\lambda - \lambda_l^{2^k}} \\ &= -2^k P_k(\lambda) \sum_{l=1}^{n} \frac{\lambda_l^{2^k-1}}{\lambda - \lambda_l^{2^k}} . \end{aligned} \tag{10.2}$$

We can obtain a recursion formula for R_{k+1} from that of Q_{k+1} by differentiating that of Q_{k+1} with respect to h and setting $h = 0$. Thus

$$R_{k+1}(\lambda) = (-1)^n [R_k(\sqrt{\lambda})\, P_k(-\sqrt{\lambda}) + R_k(-\sqrt{\lambda})\, P_k(\sqrt{\lambda})] . \tag{10.3}$$

---

* See Lehmer, [29].

Now

$$P_k(\lambda) = (-1)^n P_k(\sqrt{\lambda})\, P_k(-\sqrt{\lambda})$$

$$P_0(\lambda) = P(\lambda)$$

$$Q_0(\lambda, h) = a_n \prod_{l=1}^{n} (\lambda - \lambda_l - h) .$$

Thus

$$R_0(\lambda) = - P'(\lambda) .$$

We can obtain a recursion formula for the coefficients of the polynomial R_k of degree $n - 1$ from (10.3). To obtain relations for the λ_k we put [see (10.2)]

$$R_k(\lambda) = b_0^k + b_1^k\lambda + \cdots + b_{n-1}^k\lambda^{n-1}$$

$$= - 2^k(a_0^k + \cdots + a_n^k\lambda^n)$$

$$\times \frac{1}{\lambda} \sum_{l=1}^{n} \lambda_l^{2^k-1} \left(1 + \frac{1}{\lambda}\lambda_l^{2^k} + \frac{1}{\lambda^2}\lambda_l^{2^{k+1}} + \frac{1}{\lambda^3}\lambda_l^{2^{k+2}} + \cdots\right).$$

Now both these expressions are Laurent series for a polynomial and must therefore be the same. Thus we have [see (9.4)]

$$b_{n-1}^k = - 2^k \left(a_n^k \sum_{l=1}^{n} \lambda_l^{2^k-1}\right)$$

$$b_{n-2}^k = - 2^k \left(a_n^k \sum_{l=1}^{n} \lambda_l^{2^{k+1}-1} + a_{n-1}^k \sum_{l=1}^{n} \lambda_l^{2^k-1}\right)$$

$$= - 2^k a_n^k \left[\left(\lambda_1^{2^{k+1}-1} + \lambda_2^{2^{k+1}-1} + \cdots\right)\right.$$

$$\left. - \left(\lambda_1^{2^k} + \lambda_2^{2^k} + \cdots\right) \left(\lambda_1^{2^k-1} + \cdots\right)\right]$$

$$= 2^k a_n^k \left(\lambda_1^{2^k}\lambda_2^{2^k-1} + \lambda_1^{2^k-1}\lambda_2^{2^k} + \cdots\right)$$

$$= 2^k a_n^k \lambda_1^{2^k}\lambda_2^{2^k} \left(\frac{1}{\lambda_2} + \frac{1}{\lambda_1} + \cdots\right) .$$

Now we know [see (9.1), (9.2)]

$$a_n^k = (a_n)^{2^k}, \qquad a_{n-1}^k = -(a_n)^{2^k} \lambda_1^{2^k} + \cdots$$

Therefore we have

$$2^k \frac{a_{n-1}^k}{b_{n-1}^k} = \lambda_1 + \text{lower order terms},$$

Similarly

$$2^k \frac{a_{n-2}^k}{b_{n-2}^k} = \frac{1}{\dfrac{1}{\lambda_1} + \dfrac{1}{\lambda_2}} + \text{lower order terms}.$$

This process could be continued and all the roots of $P(\lambda)$ determined.

11. Graeffe Process Applied to Eigenvalues of Matrices and Zeros of Analytic Functions

The process of forming symetric functions of the roots of an equation becomes particularly simple if the equation to be solved is the *characteristic equation of a matrix.* Let $a = (a_{ik})$, then

$$P(\lambda) = |\lambda I - a| = \prod_{k=1}^{n} (\lambda - \lambda_k) = 0 .$$

We shall not have to evaluate this determinant in order to find the roots.

We note that

$$|\lambda I - a^2| = \prod_{k=1}^{n} (\lambda - \lambda_k^2)$$

$$|\lambda I - a^m| = \prod_{k=1}^{n} (\lambda - \lambda_k^m) .$$

Moreover let the trace of the matrix a^m be given by

$$\alpha_m = \operatorname{tr}(a)^m = \lambda_1^m + \lambda_2^m + \cdots + \lambda_n^m .$$

Therefore for large m if $|\lambda_1| > |\lambda_2| > \cdots > |\lambda_n|$ we have

$$\frac{\alpha_{m+1}}{\alpha_m} = \lambda_1 \left[1 + 0\left(\left|\frac{\lambda_2}{\lambda_1}\right|^m\right)\right] \quad \text{and} \quad \lim_{m\to\infty} \frac{\alpha_m}{\alpha_{m-1}} = \lambda_1 .$$

Similarly, applying the technique used for Bernouilli's Method [see (7.2)]:

$$\lim_{m\to\infty} \frac{\begin{vmatrix} \alpha_{m+2} & \alpha_{m+1} \\ \alpha_{m+1} & \alpha_m \end{vmatrix}}{\begin{vmatrix} \alpha_{m+1} & \alpha_m \\ \alpha_m & \alpha_{m-1} \end{vmatrix}} = \lambda_1\lambda_2$$

if $\lambda_1 \neq \lambda_2$ even if $|\lambda_1| = |\lambda_2|$.

Thus approximations for the characteristic roots can be obtained from the traces of successive powers of $\mathscr{a}$.

The Graeffe method can be adapted to finding the zeros of an analytic function. Let $f(z)$ be regular for $|z| \leqslant r$ and have zeros $z_1, z_2, \cdots, z_n$ in the circle $|z| \leqslant r$ about zero with

$$0 < |z_1| < |z_2| < \cdots < |z_n| .$$

Then in this circle

$$\begin{aligned} f(z) &= a_0 + a_1 z + a_2 z^2 + \cdots + \cdot\cdot \\ &= \left[\prod_{k=1}^{n} \left(1 - \frac{z}{z_k}\right)\right] g(z) \end{aligned}$$

($g(z) \neq 0$ for $|z| \leqslant r$). Then we can write $g(z) = e^{h(z)}$ where, $h(z)$ is analytic for $|z| \leqslant r$. Thus

$$h(z) = c_0 + c_1 z + c_2 z^2 + \cdots$$

converges inside the circle $|z| \leqslant r$. Now

$$f(z) = \left[\prod_{k=1}^{n} \left(1 - \frac{z}{z_k}\right)\right] e^{h(z)} .$$

We define

$$f^{(1)}(z) = f(\sqrt{z})f(-\sqrt{z})$$

$$= \left[\prod_{k=1}^{n}\left(1 - \frac{z}{z_k^2}\right)\right] \exp 2(c_0 + c_2 z + c_4 z^2 + \cdots)$$

$$f^{k+1}(z) = f^{(k)}(\sqrt{z})f^{(k)}(-\sqrt{z}).$$

Thus

$$f^{(k)}(z) = \prod_{l=1}^{n}\left(1 - \frac{z}{z_l^{2^k}}\right) \exp 2^k(c_0 + c_{2^k} z + c_{2.2^k} z^2 + \cdots)$$

$$= a_0^k + a_1^k z + a_2^k z^2 + \cdots$$

This is a power series which converges in a certain region. Equating both sides gives

$$a_0^k = \exp(2^k c_0)$$

$$a_k^1 = \left(2^k c_{2^k} - \sum_l z_l^{-2^k}\right) \exp(2^k c_0)$$

since $c_{2^k} = 0(r^{-2^k})$ we find that

$$\frac{a_1^k}{a_0^k} = -z_1^{-2^k} + \text{terms of higher order.}$$

Similarly relations for z_2, z_3, $\cdots$ can be obtained.

12. Iteration Schemes for Solving Systems of Equations

We shall now consider iteration methods applied to systems of n equations in n unknowns in order to obtain the roots of the system.

Consider $f_i(x_1, \cdots, x_n) = 0$ $(i = 1, \cdots, n)$ and let us write $x = (x_1, \cdots, x_n)$ and $f = (f_1, \cdots, f_n)$. Then we seek the solution of $f(x) = 0$ by means of a suitable iteration scheme. We shall use a heuristic argument to determine what conditions such a scheme must satisfy. We will then investigate the possibility of the existence of such a scheme under these conditions.

We should utilize a recursion formula $x^{k+1} = \phi(x^k)$ where ϕ is a vector function. Moreover, we require that if x is a solution of $x = \phi(x)$, then $f(x) = 0$. This leads to $x - \phi(x) = A(x) f(x)$ where $A(x)$ is a non-singular n by n matrix and

$$\phi(x) = x - A(x) f(x) . \tag{12.1}$$

We are given an x^0 and have

$$x^{k+1} - x^k = \phi(x^k) - \phi(x^{k-1}) . \tag{12.2}$$

Our requirement that x^k converge to a solution leads to

$$\lim_{k \to \infty} (x^{k+1} - x^k) = 0.$$

More precisely, we would like $x^{k+1} - x^k$ to go to zero as a geometric series, in the sense that

$$N(x^{k+1} - x^k) \leqslant qN(x^k - x^{k-1})$$

where $q < 1$ and N is a suitable natural norm. This would be the case if

$$N(\phi(y) - \phi(z)) \leqslant q(y - z)$$

which leads to a Lipschitz condition on the components of ϕ. Now for ϕ defined on the line segment joining the points y and z

$$\begin{aligned}\phi_i(y) - \phi_i(z) &= \phi_i(z + t(y - z))_{t=1} - \phi_i(z + t(y - z))_{t=0} \\ &= \int_0^1 \frac{d}{dt} \phi_i(z + t(y - z))\, dt \\ &= \int_0^1 \sum_k \frac{\partial \phi_i(z + t(y - z))}{\partial x_k} (y_k - z_k)\, dt .\end{aligned}$$

Introduce $B(x) = \left(\frac{\partial \phi_i}{\partial x_k}\right) = (B_{ik})$ which is an n by n matrix.

Thus

$$\phi_i(y) - \phi_i(z) = \int_0^1 \sum_k B_{ik}(z + t(y - z))\,(y_k - z_k)\,dt$$

and, in vector notation,

$$\phi(y) - \phi(z) = \int_0^1 [B(z + t(y - z))]\,(y - z)\,dt\,.$$

Then

$$N(\phi(y) - \phi(z)) \leqslant \int_0^1 N[B(z + t(y - z))\,(y - z)]\,dt$$

$$\leqslant \int_0^1 N[B(z + t(y - z))]\,N(y - z)\,dt\,.$$

If $N(B(x)) \leqslant q < 1$ in a convex domain R we have

$$N(\phi(y) - \phi(z)) \leqslant q \cdot N(y - z) \qquad \text{for} \qquad y \in R \quad \text{and} \quad z \in R. \tag{12.3}$$

Naturally, we impose the condition that $x^0 \in R$ and $\phi(x)$ must be defined on R. We also want to make sure that our iteration does not lead to values outside of R. Assume $x^1, \cdots, x^k$ have been constructed from x^0 by $x^{l+1} = \phi(x^l)$ $(l = 1, \cdots, k - 1)$ and that $x^0, \cdots, x^k$ are in R. We ask what conditions are sufficient to keep x^{k+1} in R. Now

$$N(x^{k+1} - x^k) \leqslant qN(x^k - x^{k-1}) \leqslant q^k N(x^1 - x^0)\,.$$

We must obviously restrict the distance of x^{k+1} from x^0. Now

$$N(x^{k+1} - x^0) \leqslant \sum_{l=0}^{k} N(x^{l+1} - x^l) \leqslant \sum_{l=0}^{n} q^l N(x^1 - x^0)$$

$$\leqslant N(x^1 - x^0)\frac{1}{1 - q} = \frac{N(\phi(x^0) - x^0)}{1 - q}\,. \tag{12.4}$$

That is x^{k+1} lies in the "sphere" around x_0 with radius $N(x^1 - x^0)/(1 - q)$. Requiring this "sphere" to lie in R is not too much of a restriction if we are already near a solution in our choice of x^0.

We now have a set of conditions that permit us to carry out the iteration scheme. Namely,

(1) $\phi(x)$ is defined and has continuous first derivatives for x in a convex domain R.

(1a) $N(B(x)) \leqslant q < 1$ for all $x \in R$.

(2) $x^0 \in R$ and the sphere $\left\{ x \mid N(x - x^0) \leqslant \frac{N(\phi(x^0) - x^0)}{1 - q} \right\} \subset R$.

Then all x^k are defined, we have

$$N(x^{k+1} - x^k) \leqslant q^k N(\phi(x^0) - x^0) \tag{12.5}$$

and the Cauchy test for convergence is satisfied, since

$$N(x^{k+l} - x^k) \leqslant \frac{q^k}{1 - q} N(x^1 - x^0) \quad \text{for} \quad l \geqslant 0 . \tag{12.6}$$

Therefore $N(x^l - x^k) \to 0$ for $k \to \infty$ and $l \to \infty$ from which we conclude that $\text{Limit}_{k \to \infty} x^k = x$ exists and, using the continuity of ϕ, that

$$x = \phi(x) .$$

Moreover, if we let $l \to \infty$ in (12.6), we obtain

$$N(x - x^k) \leqslant \frac{q^k}{1 - q} N(x^1 - x^0) . \tag{12.7}$$

Now, since $x = \phi(x)$ and $| A | \neq 0$ at x we have in x a solution of $f(x) = 0$. We have thus shown the existence of a solution utilizing the iteration scheme provided we can satisfy conditions (1), (1a) and (2).

It remains, however, to show how we can obtain an A and satisfy (1), (1a) and (2). Moreover, we wish to proceed by numerical computation, which adds the burden of a computational error to our problem. Our computational recursion formula is actually $y^{k+1} = \phi(y^k) + \epsilon^k$ where $y^0 = x^0$ and, as before, x^k satisfies $\phi(x^k) = x^{k+1}$. We further may assume that our individual computing error is uniformly bounded:

$$N(\epsilon^k) \leqslant \epsilon .$$

Now

$$y^{k+1} - x^{k+1} = \phi(y^k) - \phi(x^k) + \epsilon^k .$$

Assume that y^l is in R up to the kth iteration. Then

$$\begin{aligned} N(y^{k+1} - x^{k+1}) &\leqslant qN(y^k - x^k) + \epsilon \\ &\leqslant q^2N(y^{k-1} - x^{k-1}) + q\epsilon + \epsilon \\ &\leqslant q^kN(y^0 - x^0) + \frac{\epsilon}{1-q} = \frac{\epsilon}{1-q} . \end{aligned} \tag{12.8}$$

Now

$$N(y^{k+1} - x^0) \leqslant N(y^{k+1} - x^{k+1}) + N(x^{k+1} - x^0) \leqslant \frac{N(x^1 - x^0) + \epsilon}{1-q} .$$

The condition we must have to keep the y's from running out of R is [see (12.4)]

(2*) $$R \supset \left\{ x \mid N(x - x^0) \leqslant \frac{\epsilon + N(x^1 - x^0)}{1-q} \right\} .$$

We shall now replace (2) by (2*) in our assumptions.
An estimate for the closeness of y^k leads to [see (12.7), (12.8)]

$$\begin{aligned} N(y^k - x) &\leqslant N(y^k - x^k) + N(x^k - x) \\ &\leqslant \frac{\epsilon + q^kN(x^1 - x^0)}{1-q} . \end{aligned}$$

In practice the process could be continued until k is so large that

$$q^k \leqslant \frac{\epsilon}{N(x^1 - x^0)}$$

and then

$$N(y^k - x) \leqslant \frac{2\epsilon}{1-q} .$$

To satisfy (1), (1a) and (2*) we take for R a sphere

$$\{y \mid N(y - x^0) \leqslant p\}$$

which automatically satisfies the convexity requirement due to the triangle inequality. Let, indeed,

$$N(y - x^0) \leqslant p \qquad \text{and} \qquad N(z - x^0) \leqslant p.$$

Then for $0 < \theta < 1$

$$N(\theta y + (1-\theta) z - x^0) \leqslant N(\theta(y - x^0) + (1-\theta)(z - x_0)) \leqslant \theta N(y - x^0) + (1-\theta) N(z - x^0) \leqslant p .$$

This choice of R reduces condition (1,a) to

$(\widetilde{1})$ $\qquad N(B(x)) \leqslant q < 1 \quad \text{for} \quad N(x - x^0) \leqslant p .$

Condition (2*) becomes

$(\widetilde{2^*})$ $\qquad \epsilon + N(x^1 - x^0) \leqslant (1-q) p .$

Now if $\phi(x) = x - A(x) f(x)$ what is $B(x)$? Since

$$\phi_i(x) = x_i - \sum A_{il} f_l(x)$$

then

$$B_{ik} = \frac{\partial \phi_i}{\partial xk} = \delta_{ik} - \sum A_{il} \frac{\partial f_l}{\partial x_k} - \sum_l \frac{\partial A_{il}}{\partial x_k} f_l .$$

Let $(\partial f_l / \partial x_k) = (F_{lk}) = F$. Then $B = I - AF - C$ where C is the matrix $(\Sigma_l f_l \, \partial A_{il} / \partial x_k)$ and C is small when f is small. Thus

$$N(B) \leqslant N(I - AF) + N(C) .$$

In order to obtain concrete conditions, let us choose $N = N_\infty$. Then

$$N_\infty(C) = \operatorname*{Max}_i \sum_k \left| \sum_l \frac{\partial A_{il}}{\partial x_k} f_l \right| \leqslant N_\infty(f) \left[\operatorname*{Max}_i \sum_{k,l} \left| \frac{\partial A_{il}}{\partial x_k} \right| \right]. \tag{12.9}$$

Assume $\Sigma_{k,l} \mid \partial A_{il} / \partial x_k \mid \leqslant M$, where M a constant, for all i and all x in question. Then

$$N_\infty(C) \leqslant M N_\infty(f) \tag{12.10}$$

and

$$N_\infty(B) \leqslant N_\infty(I - AF) + N_\infty(C) \leqslant N_\infty(I - AF) + M N_\infty(f). \tag{12.11}$$

We note here that if $N_\infty(I - AF) < 1$ then $\mid A \mid \neq 0$, for otherwise $\mid A \mid = 0$ would imply $\mid AF \mid = 0$ and then for some vector ξ: $AF\xi = 0$ and thus $(I - AF)\, \xi = \xi$.

Therefore if $\xi \neq 0$

$$N(\xi) = N[(I - AF)\,\xi] \leqslant N(I - AF)\,N(\xi) < N(\xi)$$

which is a contradiction.

We observe that

$$x^1 = \phi(x^0) = x^0 - A(x^0)\,f(x^0).$$

Thus

$$x^1 - x^0 = -\,A(x^0)\,f(x^0)$$

and

$$N(x^1 - x^0) \leqslant N(A(x^0))\,N(f(x^0))\,.$$

Therefore $(\widetilde{2^*})$ is satisfied, if

$$\epsilon + N_\infty(A(x^0))\,N_\infty(f(x^0)) \leqslant (1 - q)\,p\,.$$

The only remaining problem is the characterization of A and its consequences.

There are two choices we shall consider: I. $A(x)$ is a constant matrix $\bar{A}$ and II. $A(x)$ is such that $I - A(x)\,F(x) = 0$ which is Newton's scheme of approximation to the roots.

I. $A =$ constant implies $M = 0$ and therefore we require $N_\infty(I - AF) \leqslant q < 1$ or A must be an approximate inverse of F. Take $A = F^{-1}(x^0)$ if $|\,F(x^0)\,| \neq 0$. This satisfies $(\widetilde{1})$ for sufficiently small p or $N_\infty(I - AF) \leqslant q < 1$ for $N_\infty(x - x^0) \leqslant p$. However, if $|\,F(x)\,| \ll 1$ then A may not satisfy $(\widetilde{2^*})$ since we need p so large that

$$\epsilon + N_\infty(F^{-1}(x^0))\,N_\infty(f(x^0)) \leqslant (1 - q)\,p$$

or equivalently $F^{-1}(x^0)$ must not be too large and $f(x^1)$ must be sufficiently small to insure that we can choose p properly.

II. Choose A variable such that $I - AF = 0$. That is $A = F^{-1}$ and thus M is a bound depending upon the first and second derivatives of $f(x)$. Thus $(\widetilde{1})$ by (12.11) reduces to $MN_\infty(f) \leqslant q < 1$ for $N_\infty(x - x^0) \leqslant p$ which is satisfied if f is small enough. Also the discussion of condition $(\widetilde{2^*})$ leads to the same situation as under I.

We give an error estimate for Newton's method. We have

$$x^{k+1} = x^k - A(x^k) f(x^k)$$

and

$$x = x - A(x^k) f(x).$$

Now, in Newton's method

$$A(x) = F^{-1}(x) .$$

Then

$$x^{k+1} - x = x^k - x - A(x^k) (f(x^k) - f(x))$$

If $f(x)$ has continuous second derivatives

$$f(x) - f(x^k) = F(x^k) (x - x^k) + 0((x - x^k)^2) .$$

Thus

$$\begin{aligned} x^{k+1} - x &= x^k - x + F^{-1}(x^k) F(x^k) (x - x^k) + 0((x - x^k)^2) \\ &= 0((x - x^k)^2) . \end{aligned}$$

That is, if we are already close to x, or equivalently our error is small, the convergence proceeds very rapidly since the error decreases quadratically.

13. Newton's Method for Scalar Equations

In the event x and f are scalars, Newton's method reduces to the following formula:

$$x^{k+1} = x^k - \frac{f(x^k)}{f'(x^k)} .$$

In this case, Newton's formula, as is well known, can be easily interpreted geometrically, since x^{k+1} is the abscissa of the point of intersection of the tangent to the curve at the point $(x^k, f(x^k))$ with the x-axis.

The above considerations hold for simple roots only. Let us assume we have a root x of multiplicity μ or

$$f(y) = (y - x)^\mu g(y) \qquad \text{where} \qquad g(x) \neq 0 .$$

Newton's formula

$$x^{k+1} = x^k - \frac{f(x^k)}{f'(x^k)}$$

gives

$$x^{k+1} - x = x^k - x - \frac{f(x^k)}{f'(x^k)}$$

$$= x^k - x - \frac{(x^k - x)^\mu g(x^k)}{\mu(x^k - x)^{\mu-1} g(x^k) + (x^k - x)^\mu g'(x^k)}$$

$$= \frac{(x^k - x)\left[\mu - 1 + (x^k - x)\dfrac{g'(x^k)}{g(x^k)}\right]}{\mu + (x^k - x)\dfrac{g'(x^k)}{g(x^k)}} .$$

If $\mu = 1$ then, as before,

$$x^{k+1} - x = 0((x^k - x)^2) .$$

If $\mu > 1$ and $x^k - x$ is small then we have

$$x^{k+1} - x = \left(\frac{\mu - 1}{\mu}\right)(x^k - x) + 0[(x^k - x)^2]$$

and $x^{k+1} - x$ will converge to zero if x^0 is close enough to x. Obviously, the convergence is not quadratic as in Newton's method with simple roots. However, a modification of Newton's method due to I. F. Ritter* will give us quadratic convergence in the case of multiple roots as follows. Take

$$x^{k+1} = x^k - \mu \frac{f(x^k)}{f'(x^k)} .$$

Then

$$x^{k+1} - x = \frac{(x^k - x)^2 \dfrac{g'(x^k)}{g(x^k)}}{\mu + (x^k - x)\dfrac{g'(x^k)}{g(x^k)}}$$

and

$$x^{k+1} - x = 0[(x^k - x)^2] .$$

This gives convergence at multiple roots similar to that at simple roots with the advantage that the factor μ accelerates the rate of convergence.

* See Ritter [36] for a more refined formula with cubic convergence.

If we have two roots of $f(x) = 0$ close together we may solve for them by first solving $f'(\xi) = 0$. Where the two roots lie close to ξ we have a fair approximation for our roots. Moreover, utilizing the Taylor series we have

$$f(x) = 0 = f(\xi) + \frac{f''(\xi)\,(x-\xi)^2}{2!} + \cdots$$

where higher order terms are very small due to $x - \xi$ being small. Thus we may profitably use the solution of the quadratic equation $f(\xi) + \frac{1}{2}(x - \xi)^2 f''(\xi) = 0$ as our x^0.

One may wish to solve a set of equations for x depending on a parameter y, e.g. to invert $y = f(x)$ or to solve $f(x, y) = 0$ for x. We may do this by applying Newton's method for each y. However, it is simpler to find one corresponding pair of values (x_0, y_0) for instance by Newton's method and then to solve the differential equation

$$f_x(x, y)\frac{dx}{dy} + f_y(x, y) = 0$$

with the initial values (x_0, y_0). It is easier to solve a differential equation numerically, as we shall see, than to solve $F(x, y) = 0$ by using Newton's method.

If we have $f(x, \lambda) = 0$ where λ is a scalar and x and f are vectors, we may solve for x in a manner similar to that above by considering the system of differential equations

$$F(x, \lambda)\frac{dx}{d\lambda} + f_\lambda(x, \lambda) = 0$$

where $F(x, \lambda)$ is the matrix $(\partial f_i/\partial x_k)$.

CHAPTER 3

Approximation of Eigenvalues of a Matrix

1. Isolating the Eigenvalues*

We have two equivalent definitions for an eigenvalue: (1) the eigenvalues of a are roots of the equation $|\lambda I - a| = 0$ or (2) the eigenvalues are numbers λ such that there exists a non-zero vector x corresponding to λ and $ax = \lambda x$.

Making use of the fact that the characteristic determinant in (1) is a polynomial in λ we can expand it and use the methods described above to evaluate its roots. This is not usually a feasible practical method.

A general theorem concerning the location of the eigenvalues of a complex matrix is due to Gershgorin.

Theorem: If

$$a = \begin{pmatrix} a_{11} & & & a_{1n} \\ a_{21} & a_{22} & & \\ & & \ddots & \\ a_{n1} & & & a_{nn} \end{pmatrix}$$

then all the eigenvalues of a lie in the union of the closed circular discs c_j in the complex plane with centers a_{jj} and radii

$$R_j = \sum_{\substack{k \\ k \neq j}} |a_{jk}| .$$

* See Taussky and Newman [38], Bodewig [3], Householder [22].

If one of the connected components of $\bigcup c_j$ contains μ of the c_j then this component contains exactly μ of the eigenvalues.

[If a is close to diagonal this method gives good approximations for the eigenvalues.

We can in some cases improve the estimates by observing that if λ is an eigenvalue of a then it also is an eigenvalue of a^* and of $T^{-1}aT$ where T is non-singular. These latter matrices may furnish smaller R_j .]

Proof:

(1) Let λ be an eigenvalue of a. Then there exists an $x \neq 0$ such that

$$\lambda x_i = \sum_k a_{ik} x_k = a_{ii} x_i + \sum_{\substack{k \\ k \neq i}} a_{ik} x_k .$$

Therefore

$$(\lambda - a_{ii})\, x_i = \sum_{\substack{k \\ k \neq i}} a_{ik} x_k .$$

Let $\bar{x}$ equal the maximum absolute value of the components of x say, $\bar{x} = | x_p | \geqslant | x_i |$ for all i. Then

$$| \lambda - a_{pp} |\, | x_p | = \sum_{\substack{k \\ k \neq p}} | a_{pk} x_k | .$$

Thus

$$| \lambda - a_{pp} | \,\bar{x} \leqslant \sum_{\substack{k \\ k \neq p}} | a_{pk} | \,\bar{x}$$

or

$$| \lambda - a_{pp} | \leqslant \sum_{\substack{k \\ k \neq p}} | a_{pk} | = R_p$$

since $\bar{x} \neq 0$ for $x \neq 0$. Therefore, $\lambda \in c_p$.

(2) Let $a = \alpha + \beta$ where α is the matrix of the diagonal elements of a and β the matrix of the remaining elements of a. Consider

$$| \lambda I - \alpha - t\beta | = P(\lambda, t) = 0 .$$

For $t = 1$ we have the characteristic equation

$$| \lambda I - a | = P(\lambda, 1) = 0 .$$

We shall consider the roots of $P(\lambda, t)$ for $0 \leqslant t \leqslant 1$. The roots of $P(\lambda, t)$ then lie in the union of the discs with centers at a_{jj} and radii tR_j.

Let now S be a connected component of $\bigcup c_j$, consisting of the discs c_{j_i} $(i = 1, \cdots, r)$ with radii R_{j_i}. Let S^* be the union of the discs $c^*_{j_i}$ with radius $R^*_{j_i} = R_{j_i} + \epsilon$ where ϵ is chosen so small that S^* has no common point with any of the other components. Then for a point λ on the boundary B^* of S^* $| \lambda - a_{ii} | > R_i$ for all i. Hence λ cannot be a root of $P(\lambda, t)$ for any t with $0 \leqslant t \leqslant 1$. In this range $P(\lambda, t)$ being a polynomial is analytic. Therefore Cauchy's formula gives the number of roots of $P(\lambda, t) = 0$ inside S^*, i.e.

$$N = \frac{1}{2\pi} \oint_{B^*} \frac{P_\lambda(\lambda, t)}{P(\lambda, t)} \, d\lambda .$$

It follows from the continuity of N that the number of roots is the same for $t = 0$ as for $t = 1$. We have for $t = 0$ exactly μ roots if there were μ of the c_j in the component S. Therefore there are exactly μ roots of $P(\lambda, 1)$ in S^*. For $\epsilon \to 0$ $S^* \to S$ and hence there are exactly μ roots in S.

Q.E.D.

We can also obtain estimates for the *eigenvectors* by an adaptation of the Gershgorin procedure. Assume the disc $| \lambda - a_{ii} | \leqslant R_i$ has no point in common with any other disc. Then there lies exactly one eigenvalue λ_i in this disc:

$$| \lambda_i - a_{ii} | \leqslant R_i$$
$$| \lambda_i - a_{kk} | > R_k \qquad k \neq i .$$

Let $(x_1, \cdots, x_n)$ be the eigenvector belonging to λ_i,

$$\sum_{l=1}^{n} a_{kl} x_l = \lambda_i x_k$$

or

$$(\lambda_i - a_{kk})\, x_k = \sum_{l \neq k} a_{kl} x_l .$$

Let X be the maximum of $|x_k|$. Then

$$|\lambda_i - a_{kk}|\,|x_k| \leqslant R_k X$$

and for $k \neq i$

$$|x_k| \leqslant \frac{R_k}{|\lambda_i - a_{kk}|} X < X .$$

Hence $X = |x_i|$. Thus we obtain for x_k, $k \neq i$, the estimate

$$\left|\frac{x_k}{x_i}\right| \leqslant \frac{R_k}{|\lambda_i - a_{kk}|} < 1 .$$

This estimate for the eigenvector is the sharper the smaller the R_k.

2. Use of Rotations*

If we have a real symmetric matrix we can use a method due to Jacobi to transform the matrix into a similar one which is nearly diagonal. We transform by using an n dimensional rotation. This is performed by a sequence of 2-dimensional rotations. Let a be our matrix. Now $a = a^*$. Let $b = T^{-1}aT$ where $T^{-1} = T^*$ (e.g. T is orthogonal). Then a and b have the same eigenvalues and traces: $\mathrm{Tr}\, a = \mathrm{Tr}\, b$. Also bb^* is similar to aa^*, that is $bb^* = T^{-1}aa^*T$. Thus $\mathrm{Tr}\, bb^* = \mathrm{Tr}\, aa^*$. This gives

$$\mathrm{Tr}\, bb^* = \sum_{i,k} b_{ik}^2 = \sum_{i,k} a_{ik}^2 = \mathrm{Tr}\, aa^* .$$

Choose i and k such that $i \neq k$ and $|a_{ik}| \geqslant |a_{rs}|$ for all $r \neq s$. For simplicity assume $i = 1$ and $k = 2$. Let T be

$$T = \begin{pmatrix} \cos\phi & \sin\phi & 0 & \cdots & \\ -\sin\phi & \cos\phi & 0 & \cdots & \\ 0 & 0 & 1 & 0 & \\ \vdots & 0 & 0 & 1 & \\ & & & & \ddots \\ & & & & & 1 \end{pmatrix}$$

* See Newman [33].

This transformation will only affect the first two rows and columns of a. By a proper choice of ϕ the sub matrix

$$\begin{pmatrix} a_{11} & a_{12} \\ a_{21} & a_{22} \end{pmatrix}$$

can be diagonalized:

$$\begin{pmatrix} b_{11} & b_{12} \\ b_{21} & b_{22} \end{pmatrix} = \begin{pmatrix} \cos\phi & -\sin\phi \\ \sin\phi & \cos\phi \end{pmatrix} \begin{pmatrix} a_{11} & a_{12} \\ a_{21} & a_{22} \end{pmatrix} \begin{pmatrix} \cos\phi & \sin\phi \\ -\sin\phi & \cos\phi \end{pmatrix}$$

and $b_{ik} = a_{ik}$ for both i and $k > 2$. If

$$\tan 2\phi = \frac{2a_{12}}{a_{22} - a_{11}}$$

then we have $b_{21} = b_{12} = 0$. (This makes sense even if $a_{11} = a_{22}$.) Thus

$$a_{11} + a_{22} = b_{11} + b_{22}$$

and

$$a_{11}^2 + 2a_{12}^2 + a_{22}^2 = b_{11}^2 + b_{22}^2$$

since $a_{12} = a_{21}$.

Since $| a_{12} |$ is maximum, and since $b_{ii}^2 = a_{ii}^2$ for $i > 2$ we have

$$\begin{aligned}\sum_{\substack{i,k\\ i\neq k}} b_{ik}^2 &= \sum_{i,k} b_{ik}^2 - \sum_{i} b_{ii}^2 \\ &= \sum_{i,k} a_{ik}^2 - \sum_{i>2} a_{ii}^2 - a_{11}^2 - a_{22}^2 - 2a_{12}^2 \\ &= \sum_{i\neq k} a_{ik}^2 - 2a_{12}^2 \leqslant \left(1 - \frac{2}{n^2 - n}\right) \sum_{\substack{i,k\\ i\neq k}} a_{ik}^2 .\end{aligned}$$

We have therefore lowered the sum of the squares of the off diagonal elements and if the off diagonal elements are not all 0 we can apply this method repeatedly.

It does not always pay to apply Jacobi's method exclusively. Instead, one may use Jacobi's and Gershgorin's theorems to separate the roots sufficiently and then proceed in some other manner.

3. Iteration Schemes

If $A = A^*$ there is again a method due to Jacobi to approximate the eigenvectors and eigenvalues by a variant of Newton's scheme. This method has the advantage that matrices are not multiplied by matrices as above, but by vectors, a much simpler operation computationally.

Assume we have an approximate eigenvalue μ and an approximate eigenvector y where the exact eigenvalue λ and eigenvector x satisfy $Ax = \lambda x$ with λ a simple root. Then we may write

$$Ay = \mu y + z \tag{3.1}$$

where z is an error term obtained by inserting μ and y. The object is to find a Δy and a $\Delta \mu$ which bring us closer to x and λ respectively. For the ideal choice

$$A(y + \Delta y) = (\mu + \Delta\mu)(y + \Delta y) .$$

Multiplying out we find that

$$z + A\Delta y = \mu\Delta y + y\Delta\mu + \Delta\mu\Delta y$$

which we rewrite

$$(A - \mu - \Delta\mu)\Delta y = -z + y\Delta\mu . \tag{3.2}$$

Then

$$(y^* + \Delta y^*)(A - \mu - \Delta\mu)\Delta y = (y^* + \Delta y^*)(-z + y\Delta\mu) . \tag{3.3}$$

We want that

$$(A - \mu - \Delta\mu)(y + \Delta y) = 0$$

or, equivalently, since $A^* = A$,

$$(y^* + \Delta y^*)(A - \mu - \Delta\mu) = 0 .$$

Therefore by (3.3)

$$-y^*z + (\Delta\mu)y^*y - (\Delta y)^*z + (\Delta y^*)(\Delta\mu)y = 0 .$$

Let us assume z, Δy, and $\Delta\mu$ are small. Then we can replace the last relation by the explicit equation

$$\Delta\mu = \frac{y^*z}{y^*y}\,. \tag{3.4}$$

To determine Δy we shall solve, instead of (3.2), since $\Delta\mu$ is small,

$$(A - \mu)\,\Delta y = -\,z + (\Delta\mu)\,y\,.$$

Since we have assumed that $|\,A - \mu\,|$ is small, we cannot solve the n equations very well numerically, but will solve only the first $n - 1$ of them. That is

$$\sum_{k=1}^{n} (A_{ik} - \mu\delta_{ik})\,\Delta y_k = -\,z_i + (\Delta\mu)y_i$$

($i = 1, 2, \cdots, n - 1$). To complete our system of equations we we shall add the condition

$$\sum_{k=1}^{n} y_k \Delta y_k = 0\,.$$

We have from (3.4) that $\Delta\mu = 0(z)$ and we shall now show the new error $\tilde{z}$ to be $0(z^2)$, where

$$\sum_k (A_{ik} - \mu\delta_{ik} - \Delta\mu\delta_{ik})\,(y_k + \Delta y_k) = \tilde{z}_i\,.$$

Now $\Delta y_k = 0(z)$ since $\Delta\mu$ and $-z$ are $0(z)$. Expanding, we have:

$$\sum_k A_{ik}y_k - \mu y_i - (\Delta\mu)y_i + \sum A_{ik}\Delta y_k - \mu\Delta y_i - \Delta\mu\Delta y_i = \tilde{z}_i\,.$$

Cancelling, we have for the first $n - 1$ components of $\tilde{z}$

$$\tilde{z}_i = z_i - z_i - \Delta\mu\Delta y_i = 0(z^2)\,.$$

We shall show that this estimate also holds for the nth component. To do this we first show

$$\sum_{i=1}^{n} y_i\tilde{z}_i = \sum_{i,k} y_i(A_{ik} - \mu\delta_{ik} - \Delta\mu\delta_{ik})\,(y_k + \Delta y_k) = 0(z^2)\,.$$

We note that since the first $n - 1$ components are $0(z^2)$; this implies for $y_n \neq 0$ that the nth component is also $0(z^2)$. Expanding, we have by (3.1), using $A_{il} = A_{ki}$,

$$\sum_{i,k} y_i(A_{ik} - \mu\delta_{ik} - \Delta\mu\delta_{ik})(y_k + \Delta y_k) = \sum_i y_i z_i - (\Delta\mu)y_i y_i$$

$$+ \sum_k (\mu y_k + z_k)\Delta y_k - \mu \sum_i y_i \Delta y_i - \Delta\mu \sum y_i \Delta y_i .$$

We have from (3.4)

$$\sum_i y_i z_i = \Delta\mu \sum_i y_i y_i .$$

Using this and reducing we obtain

$$\sum_{i,k} y_i(A_{ik} - \mu\delta_{ik} - \Delta\mu\delta_{ik})(y_k + \Delta y_k) = 0(z^2) .$$

This establishes our result if we assume $y_n \neq 0$.

Methods also exist for non-symmetric matrices (provided they have distinct eigenvalues) that permit to obtain approximations for eigenvectors and eigenvalues. Choose a vector X^0 and define

$$X^k = (A)^k X^0 \qquad (k = 1, 2 \cdots) .$$

We shall show for $k \to \infty$ the direction of x^k approaches that of an eigenvector. Since by assumption the eigenvalues are distinct, we know that A has n independent eigenvectors $y^1, \cdots, y^n$ corresponding to eigenvalues $\lambda_1, \cdots \lambda_n$. Thus

$$Ay^l = \lambda_l y^l \qquad (l = 1, 2, \cdots, n) .$$

Here we can write

$$X^0 = c_1 y^1 + \cdots + c_n y^n$$

due to independence. It follows that

$$X^k = c_1 \lambda_1{}^k y^1 + \cdots + c_n \lambda_n{}^k y^n .$$

Let $c_1 \neq 0$ and $|\lambda_1| > |\lambda_l|$ for $l > 1$. Then we have, rewriting the above as

$$X^k = c_1\lambda_1^k\left(y^1 + \frac{c_2}{c_1} y^2 \frac{\lambda_2^k}{\lambda_1^k} + \cdots + \frac{c_n}{c_1} y^n \frac{\lambda_n^k}{\lambda_1^k}\right)$$

that the direction of X^k converges to the direction of y^1 as k goes to ∞. If we now consider the first component of X^{k+1} and X^k we obtain assuming $y_1^1 \neq 0$

$$\lim_{k\to\infty} \frac{X_1^{k+1}}{X_1^k} = \lambda_1$$

This method can be generalized to the second largest eigenvalue, etc., as in Bernouilli's scheme. However, we may employ a simple device which will make any eigenvalue, λ_s, which we assume we know approximately, the largest eigenvalue. Let μ be the approximation to λ_s and consider instead of A the matrix $B = (\mu I - A)^{-1}$. It is easy to show its eigenvalues are $1/(\mu - \lambda_j)$ $(j = 1, \cdots n)$. Assume that μ lies closer to λ_s than to any other λ_j. Then $1/(\mu - \lambda_s)$ is the maximum eigenvalue of B and may be computed as above since the eigenvectors of A and B are the same. Thus for $X^k = B^k X^0$

$$\lim_{k\to\infty} \frac{X_1^{k+1}}{X_1^k} = \frac{1}{\mu - \lambda_s}.$$

and since we know μ we may solve for λ_s.

If μ is too good a guess for λ_s then $(\mu I - A)^{-1}$ will be difficult to evaluate. Therefore we do not want too close an approximation μ for λ_s.

We can avoid calculating B explicitly by solving a system of equations at each step since $(\mu I - A) X^{k+1} = X^k$.

The general principle of which the above is a special case is: Instead of A compute a suitable function $f(A)$. Then the eigenvectors remain the same; in order to use the above procedure take f so that

$$\left|\frac{f(\lambda_j)}{f(\lambda_s)}\right| \ll 1 \qquad \text{for} \qquad j \neq s.$$

CHAPTER 4

Approximation of Functions.*

The problem we now propose to solve is as follows: Given a finite number of values of a function $f(x)$ corresponding to $x_0, \cdots, x_n$ find some method of determining $f(x)$ at points other than the given ones with a degree of accuracy sufficient for our purposes.

A related problem occurs when we know $f(x)$ approximately, say by measurement, for a large number of values and wish to find a function which approximates $f(x)$ at all other points. Similarly, we might wish to find a function which smoothes out the irregularities in our empirical $f(x)$ while approximating its measured values.

The procedure usually followed is to choose a system of simple functions $\psi_l(x)$; $l = 0, 1, \cdots n$ and to solve the system of equations

$$f(x_i) = \sum_{l=0}^{n} c_l \psi_l(x_i);$$

$(i = 0, \cdots, n)$ for c_l; $(l = 0, 1, \cdots, n)$. We then have a representation for our function

$$f(x) = \sum_{l=1}^{n} c_l \psi_l(x)$$

which is correct at least at each of the x_i, $(i = 0, \cdots, n)$.

1. Lagrange Interpolation Formula

We shall consider the case where $\psi_l(x) = x^l$ or, equivalently, seek a polynomial representation of our function. We assume we

* See Householder [21], Davis [9], Isaacson and Keller [23].

are given distinct values x_0, x_1, $\cdots$, x_m for the independent variable and the values of the function at these points $f(x_0)$, $\cdots$, $f(x_m)$. The problem is then to find a polynomial P_m of degree $\leqslant m$ such that $P_m(x_k) = f(x_k)$ for $k = 0, 1, \cdots, m$. We can write this condition as

$$P_m(x) = \sum_{k=0}^{m} f(x_k)\, p_k^m(x)$$

where the p_k^m are polynomials of degree m that have to be determined from the conditions

$$p_k^m(x) = \begin{cases} 0 & \text{for} \quad x = x_l \qquad l \neq k. \\ 1 & \text{for} \quad x = x_k\,, \end{cases}$$

The solution to the above problem is given by the *Lagrange Interpolation polynomials*:

$$p_k^m(x) = \frac{\prod\limits_{\substack{l=0\\ l\neq k}}^{m} (x - x_l)}{\prod\limits_{\substack{l=0\\ l\neq k}}^{m} (x_k - x_l)}. \tag{1.1}$$

If we introduce the expression

$$\omega_m(x) = \prod_{l=0}^{m} (x - x_l)\,, \tag{1.2}$$

which is a polynomial of degree $m + 1$, we have

$$p_k^m(x) = \frac{\omega_m(x)}{(x - x_k)\,\omega_m'(x_k)} \tag{1.3}$$

and the *Lagrange Interpolation formula* takes the form

$$P_m(x) = \sum_{k=0}^{m} \frac{\omega_m(x)}{(x - x_k)\,\omega_m'(x_k)} f(x_k)\,. \tag{1.4}$$

2. Newton's Interpolation Formula

We can find a different expansion for $P_m(x)$ of the form

$$P_m(x) = \sum_{l=0}^{m} \frac{a_l}{l!} \omega_{l-1}(x) \tag{2.1}$$

where again for $l \geqslant 0$

$$\omega_l(x) = (x - x_0)(x - x_1) \cdots (x - x_l) \tag{2.2}$$

and we define $\omega_{-1}(x) = +1$. This is possible since the $\omega_i(x)$ are linearly independent polynomials. We can always determine the coefficients a_j in (2.1) in such a way that $P_m(x_j) = f(x_j)$ for $j = 0, \cdots, m$ without using the expressions (1.4).

If we introduce the partial sums

$$P_k(x) = \sum_{l=0}^{k} \frac{a_l}{l!} \omega_{l-1}(x) \tag{2.3}$$

for $k = 0, \cdots, m$ we clearly have in $P_k(x)$ a polynomial of degree k for which

$$P_k(x_i) = P_m(x_i) = f(x_i) \qquad \text{for} \quad 0 \leqslant i \leqslant k \leqslant m.$$

Therefore

$$P_{k+1}(x) = P_k(x) + p(x) = P_k(x) + \frac{a_{k+1}}{(k+1)!} \omega_k(x) \tag{2.4}$$

where the correction term $p(x)$ has to reduce to $f(x_{k+1}) - P_k(x_{k+1})$ for $x = x_{k+1}$ and hence is given by

$$\frac{\omega_k(x)}{\omega_k(x_{k+1})} [f(x_{k+1}) - P_k(x_{k+1})].$$

Therefore the polynomials $P_k(x)$ and coefficients a_k are independent of m and can be computed successively from (2.4) and the formula

$$a_{k+1} = (k+1)! \frac{[f(x_{k+1}) - P_k(x_{k+1})]}{\omega_k(x_{k+1})}. \tag{2.5}$$

If we go back to the Lagrange expression (1.4) for $P_m(x)$ and compute the highest order term we have

$$P_m(x) = x^m \sum_{k=0}^{m} \frac{f(x_k)}{\omega_m'(x_k)} + \cdots \tag{2.5a}$$

and therefore by comparison with (2.1)

$$\sum_{k=0}^{m} \frac{f(x_k)}{\omega_m'(x)} = \frac{a_m}{m!}, \tag{2.6}$$

We see from this that a_m is a linear combination of the values $f(x)$ at the points $x_0, \cdots, x_m$. Multiplying both sides by

$$(x_m - x_0) = (x_m - x_k) + (x_k - x_0)$$

we get

$$\frac{a_m}{m!}(x_m - x_0) = \sum_{k=0}^{m} \frac{f(x_k)}{\omega_m'(x_k)}(x_m - x_k) + \sum_{k=0}^{m} \frac{f(x_k)}{\omega_m'(x_k)}(x_k - x_0). \tag{2.7}$$

We introduce the notation

$$a_m = f[x_0, \cdots, x_m] = m! \sum_{k=0}^{m} \frac{f(x_k)}{\omega_m'(x_k)} = m! \sum_{k=0}^{m} \frac{f(x_k)}{\prod\limits_{\substack{l=0 \\ l\neq k}}^{m} (x_k - x_l)} \tag{2.8}$$

for the n-th *divided difference* of f. We can write (2.7) in the form

$$\frac{a_m}{m!}(x_m - x_0) = -\sum_{k=0}^{m-1} \frac{f(x_k)}{\prod\limits_{\substack{l=0 \\ l\neq k}}^{m-1} (x_k - x_l)} + \sum_{k=1}^{m} \frac{f(x_k)}{\prod\limits_{\substack{l=1 \\ l\neq k}}^{m} (x_k - x_l)}$$

or

$$\frac{f[x_0, \cdots, x_m]}{m!}(x_m - x_0) = \frac{-1}{m - 1)!} f[x_0, \cdots, x_{m-1}] + \frac{1}{(m-1)!} f[x_1, \cdots, x_m].$$

We have, therefore, the recursion formula

$$f[x_0, \cdots, x_m] = \frac{f[x_1, \cdots, x_m] - f[x_0, \cdots, x_{m-1}]}{\dfrac{(x_m - x_0)}{m}}. \tag{2.9}$$

If we use that $f[x_0] = f(x_0)$ the formula gives successively

$$f[x_0, x_1] = \frac{f(x_1) - f(x_0)}{x_1 - x_0} \tag{2.10}$$

$$f[x_0, x_1, x_2] = \frac{\dfrac{f(x_2) - f(x_1)}{x_2 - x_1} - \dfrac{f(x_1) - f(x_0)}{x_1 - x_0}}{\dfrac{x_2 - x_0}{2}}.$$

In this notation formula (2.1) for the interpolation polynomial takes Newton's form

$$P_m(x) = f[x_0] + \frac{f[x_0, x_1]}{1!}(x - x_0) + \frac{f[x_0, x_1, x_2]}{2!}(x - x_0)(x - x_1)$$

$$+ \cdots + \frac{f[x_0, x_1, \cdots, x_m]}{m!} \prod_{l=0}^{m-1} (x - x_l). \tag{2.12}$$

In the special case of *equidistant* points $x_k = x_0 + kh$ we have here by (2.8) the expression

$$f[x_0, \ldots, x_k] = \sum_{j=0}^{k} (-1)^{k-j} h^{-k} \binom{k}{j} f(x_j) \tag{2.13}$$

for the k-th divided difference.

3. Representation and Estimate for the Remainder Term

In general $P_m(x)$ is not an exact representation of $f(x)$ for x not equal to $x_0, \cdots, x_m$ so that there is a remainder:

$$f(x) = P_m(x) + R_m(x). \tag{3.1}$$

We wish to find an expression for R_m. Now, by (2.12) if m is replaced by $m + 1$ and x by x_{m+1}:

$$f(x_{m+1}) = P_{m+1}(x_{m+1})$$

$$= P_m(x_{m+1}) + \frac{(x_{m+1} - x_0) \cdots (x_{m+1} - x_m)}{(m + 1)!} f[x_0, \cdots, x_{m+1}].$$

Since x_{m+1} is independent of $x_0, \cdots, x_m$ we may reinsert x for it and have for the remainder

$$R_m(x) = \frac{(x - x_0) \cdots (x - x_m)}{(m + 1)!} f[x_0, x_1, \cdots, x_m, x] . \tag{3.2}$$

Now $f(x) - P_m(x) = 0$ for $x = x_0, x_1, \cdots, x_m$ and consequently $d^m R_m(x)/dx^m$ vanishes for at least one point ξ within the smallest interval containing $x_0, \cdots, x_m$. Then by (2.5a), (2.6)

$$\frac{d^m f(\xi)}{dx^m} - \frac{d^m P_m(\xi)}{dx^m} = \frac{d^m f(\xi)}{dx^m} - m! \sum_{k=0}^{m} \frac{f(x_k)}{\omega_m'(x_k)} = \frac{d^m f(\xi)}{dx^m} - a_m = 0$$

which gives

$$f[x_0, \cdots, x_m] = \frac{d^m f(\xi)}{dx^m} . \tag{3.3}$$

Therefore by (3.2)

$$R_m(x) = \frac{(x - x_0) \cdots (x - x_m)}{(m + 1)!} \frac{d^{m+1} f(\xi)}{dx^{m+1}} \tag{3.4}$$

where ξ is a point in the smallest interval containing $x_0, \cdots, x_m, x$.

The error has the same form as the error term in the Taylor formula. In fact, Taylor's formula is the limiting case obtained from the interpolation formula (2.12) when $x_1, \cdots, x_m$ merge with x_0 and we obtain

$$f(x) = f(x_0) + \cdots + \frac{(x - x_0)^m}{m!} \frac{d^m f(x_0)}{dx^m} + \frac{(x - x_0)^{m+1}}{(m + 1)!} \frac{d^{m+1} f(\zeta)}{dx^{m+1}}$$

where ζ is in general a point between x_0 and x. It can be seen that the error term R_m for the interpolation polynomials may be smaller than that for the Taylor's series since often

$$(x - x_0)^{m+1} > (x - x_0) \cdots (x - x_m) .$$

We can consider for example the interval from -1 to $+1$ and let $x_0, \cdots, x_m$ be the zeros of the Chebyshev polynomial $T_{m+1}(x) = 0$. The Chebyshev polynomials are defined as follows.

Consider cos $n\theta$ expanded as a polynomial in terms of cos θ:

$$\cos n\theta = T_n(\cos \theta) \tag{3.5}$$

and replace cos θ by x forming $T_n(x)$. Then $T_n(x) = \cos(n[\text{arc}\cos x])$ is the Chebyshev polynomial.* It can easily be shown that

$$T_{m+1}(x) = 2^m x^{m+1} + \cdots = 2^m(x - x_0)(x - x_1)\cdots(x - x_m) \tag{3.6}$$

where $x_0, \cdots, x_m$ are the zeros of $T_{m+1}(x)$. This follows from the trigonometric identity

$$\cos(n+1)\theta + \cos(n-1)\theta = 2\cos\theta\cos n\theta$$

which yields the recursion formula

$$T_{n+1}(x) + T_{n-1}(x) = 2xT_n(x)\,. \tag{3.7}$$

if we still use that $T_0(x) = 1$, $T_1(x) = x$. It is simple to compute the zeros of $T_{m+1}(x) = 0$ since we have

$$T_{m+1}(\cos\theta) = \cos[(m+1)\theta]$$

and cos $[(m + 1)\,\theta]$ vanishes where

$$(m+1)\,\theta = \frac{\pi}{2} + k\pi$$

which gives

$$\theta = \frac{\pi}{2}\left(\frac{1+2k}{m+1}\right).$$

If we take

$$x_k = \cos\frac{\pi}{2}\left(\frac{1+2k}{m+1}\right) \tag{3.8}$$

for $k = 0, \cdots, m$ we have obtained all the zeros of $T_{m+1}(x) = 0$.

From

$$T_{m+1}(x) = \cos[(m+1)\,\theta]$$

* Sometimes $T_n(\cos\theta)$ is defined by $2^{1-n}\cos n\theta$.

we obtain for $x = \cos\theta$, i.e. for $|x| \leqslant 1$,

$$|T_{m+1}(x)| = |\cos[(m+1)\theta]) \leqslant 1.$$

This gives by (3.6)

$$|(x - x_0) \cdots (x - x_m)| = \frac{1}{2^m}|T_m(x)| \leqslant \frac{1}{2^m} \qquad \text{for} \qquad |x| \leqslant 1$$

from which we obtain in the interval $-1 \leqslant x \leqslant 1$

$$|R_m(x)| \leqslant \frac{1}{(m+1)!\,2^m}\frac{df^{m+1}(\zeta)}{dx^{m+1}}; \qquad \text{where} \qquad |\zeta| \leqslant 1\,. \qquad (3.9)$$

It can be shown that the Chebyshev polynomials give the best possible estimate in this context for $R_m(x)$. It is seen that the remainder for the Taylor's series may be 2^m times as large.

4. Limitations on the Use of Interpolation Polynomials as Approximations

Generally, the interpolatory polynomial of degree m, belonging to a function $f(x)$ is given by

$$P_m(x) = \sum_{k=0}^{m} \frac{(x - x_0)(x - x_1) \cdots (x - x_{k-1})}{k!} f[x_0, \cdots, x_k]\,. \qquad (4.1)$$

One might think that, at least for analytic $f(x)$, the infinite series

$$\sum_{k=0}^{\infty} \frac{(x - x_0)(x - x_1) \cdots (x - x_{k-1})}{k!} f[x_0, \cdots, x_k]$$

would converge towards $f(x)$. This is, however, in general, not true. Take, for example, $f(x) = e^x$ and equally spaced points $x_k = x_0 + kh$. Then by (2.13)

$$f[x_0, \cdots, x_k] = e^{x_0}\left(\frac{e^h - 1}{h}\right)^k.$$

For $x = x_0 + h/2$ the $(k+1)$st term of the series exceeds in absolute value

$$\frac{\frac{1}{2}h\,(\frac{1}{2}h)\,(\frac{3}{2}h)\cdots(kh-\frac{3}{2}h)}{k!}\,e^{x_0}\left(\frac{e^h-1}{h}\right)^k$$

$$\geqslant \frac{1}{4}\,\frac{1}{k(k-1)}\,e^{x_0}\,(e^h-1)^k\,.$$

For convergence the last expression would have to have the limit zero as $k \to \infty$. Therefore we must have $|\,e^h - 1\,| \leqslant 1$ and therefore h must not exceed log. 2.

Even when $h \to 0$ as $m \to \infty$ the interpolatory polynomials do not have to converge towards a function.* Runge gives the example of the function

$$f(x) = \frac{1}{1+25x^2}$$

which is analytic for all real x. He considers the interpolation polynomial $P_m(x)$ of degree m coinciding with $f(x)$ on the points obtained by dividing the interval $[-1, 1]$ into m equal parts and proves that the $P_m(x)$ diverge for $m \to \infty$ when $|\,x\,| > \cdot 726$. This shows that even a very regular function does not have to be approximated closely by the polynomial of degree m coinciding with $f(x)$ on $m+1$ points, at least if the points are equidistant. Interpolation polynomials based on too many points may lead to very poor approximations. The reason for the divergence in this particular example lies in the presence of the imaginary singularities $x = \pm i/5$. We shall prove later that the interpolation polynomials converge for analytic $f(x)$ if the singularities are sufficiently far away from the interpolation points.

5. Sufficient Conditions for Convergence of Interpolation Polynomials. Numerical Analytic Continuation

Classical analytic continuation if performed by taking the power series expansion of an analytic function $f(z)$ about some point z_i, i.e.

$$f(z) = \sum_{k=0}^{\infty} \frac{f^{(k)}(z_i)}{k!}\,(z-z_i)^k\,,$$

* See Runge [37].

and then finding from this coefficients for a new series about some new point z_{i+1} within the circle of convergence of the old series. We can determine $f(z)$ exactly if we have its values at an infinite number of points with one point of accumulation. Quite naturally, if we have only a finite number of values of $f(z)$, say at $z_0, \cdots, z_n$ we can try to form an approximation by the use of polynomials.

The interpolation polynomials P_m corresponding to given $z_0, \cdots, z_m$ are

$$P_m(z) = \sum_{k=0}^{m} \frac{\phi(z) f(z_k)}{\phi'(z_k)(z - z_k)}$$

where

$$\phi(z) = \omega_m(z) = \prod_{k=0}^{m} (z - z_k) . \tag{5.1}$$

We can write $P_m(z)$ also as a contour integral in the complex ζ-plane:

$$P_m(z) = \frac{1}{2\pi i} \oint_{\mathcal{C}} \frac{\phi(z) - \phi(\zeta)}{\phi(\zeta)(z - \zeta)} f(\zeta)\, d\zeta \tag{5.2}$$

where $\mathcal{C}$ encloses all the points z_i $(i = 0, \cdots, m)$ and the point z. This is seen as follows: for every ζ the integrand is a polynomial of degree m in z, hence the whole integral is a polynomial of degree $\leqslant m$ in z. Moreover for $z = z_k$, $\phi(z) = 0$ and the expression reduces to $f(z_k)$ by Cauchy's formula.

For the error we have

$$f(z) - P_m(z) = \frac{1}{2\pi i} \oint_{\mathcal{C}} \frac{f(\zeta)}{\zeta - z} \left[1 + \frac{\phi(z) - \phi(\zeta)}{\phi(\zeta)}\right] d\zeta .$$

This gives

$$f(z) - P_m(z) = \frac{1}{2\pi i} \oint_{\mathcal{C}} \frac{\phi(z) f(\zeta)}{\phi(\zeta)(\zeta - z)}\, d\zeta . \tag{5.3}$$

We want an estimate for this error. We note that

$$\frac{\phi(z)}{\phi(\zeta)} = \prod_{k=0}^{m} \frac{z - z_k}{\zeta - z_k} .$$

If $|z - z_k| \leqslant q|\zeta - z_k|$ where $q < 1$ for $k = 0, 1, \cdots, m$ and all ζ on $\mathfrak{C}$ we would have

$$\left|\frac{\phi(z)}{\phi(\zeta)}\right| \leqslant q^{m+1}.$$

If we assume $|f(z)| \leqslant M$ inside $\mathfrak{C}$ (by assumption f is analytic) we have the estimate for the error

$$|f(z) - P_m(z)| \leqslant \frac{q^{m+1}}{2\pi} M \oint_{\mathfrak{C}} \left|\frac{d\zeta}{\zeta - z}\right|. \tag{5.4}$$

This clearly goes to zero for $m \to \infty$.

As a concrete instance let $f(z)$ be analytic for $|z| \leqslant R$ and $|f(z)| \leqslant M$ for $|z| \leqslant R$. Let $\mathfrak{C}$ be the circle of radius R and restrict the z_k such that $|z_k| \leqslant R/4$ for $k = 0, 1, \cdots, m$. Consider z such that $|z| \leqslant R/4$, then $|z - z_k| \leqslant R/2$ and $|\zeta - z_k| \geqslant 3R/4$ This permits to take $q = 2/3$ so that by (5.4)

$$|f(z) - P_m(z)| \leqslant (\tfrac{2}{3})^{m+1} M(\tfrac{4}{3}). \tag{5.5}$$

6. Interpolation and Continuation Based on Approximate Data

If instead of the precise values $f(z_k)$ only approximations ζ_k are given such that $|f(z_k) - \zeta_k| \leqslant \epsilon$ we define the interpolation corresponding to the ζ_k by

$$\tilde{P}_m(z) = \sum_{k=0}^{m} \frac{\phi(z)}{\phi'(z_k)} \left(\frac{\zeta_k}{z - z_k}\right).$$

We have then

$$|P_m(z) - \tilde{P}_m(z)| \leqslant \epsilon \sum_{k=0}^{m} \left|\frac{\phi(z)}{\phi'(z_k)} \cdot \frac{1}{(z - z_k)}\right|. \tag{6.1}$$

We need an estimate for $\phi(z)/\phi'(z_k)$. For convenience we specialize to z_k which are all on the real axis and equidistant. That is let z_0, $z_1, \cdots, z_m$ lie in the interval $-R/4$ to $R/4$ and $z_{k+1} - z_k = h$ for

$k = 0, 1, \cdots, m-1$. Then $\theta = mh/R \leqslant \frac{1}{2}$. For $|z| < R/4$

$$\left|\frac{\phi(z)}{z - z_k}\right| = \left|\prod_{\substack{j=0\\j\neq k}}^{m} (z - z_j)\right| \leqslant \left(\frac{R}{2}\right)^m$$

and

$$|\phi'(z_k)| = \prod_{\substack{j=0\\j\neq k}}^{m} |z_j - z_k| = \prod_{\substack{j=0\\j\neq k}}^{m} |k - j|\, h = h^m k!(m-k)!\,.$$

We now have for our original expression (6.1) the estimate

$$|P_m(z) - \tilde{P}_m(z)| \leqslant \epsilon \sum_{k=0}^{m} \left|\frac{\phi(z)}{\phi'(z_k)} \cdot \frac{1}{z - z_k}\right|$$

$$\leqslant \frac{\epsilon}{m!}\left(\frac{R}{2h}\right)^m \sum_{k=0}^{m} \frac{m!}{k!(m-k)!}$$

$$= \frac{\epsilon}{m!}\left(\frac{R}{h}\right)^m \leqslant \frac{\epsilon}{\sqrt{2\pi m}}\left(\frac{eR}{mh}\right)^m = \frac{\epsilon}{\sqrt{2m\pi}}\left(\frac{e}{\theta}\right)^m$$

where we have used $m! \geqslant \sqrt{2\pi m}\,(m/e)^m$ from Stirling's formula.

We thus have as an estimate for the total error E involved in using this approximation [see (5.5)]:

$$E = |f(z) - \tilde{P}_m(z)| \leqslant \tfrac{4}{3}\left(\tfrac{2}{3}\right)^{m+1} M + \frac{\epsilon}{\sqrt{2\pi m}}\left(\frac{e}{\theta}\right)^m.$$

A crude optimum value of m may be obtained by taking the largest integer not exceeding the real number for which

$$\left(\tfrac{2}{3}\right)^m M = \epsilon\left(\frac{e}{\theta}\right)^m$$

which gives, provided $\epsilon < 2\theta M/3e$,

$$m = \frac{\log\left(\dfrac{M}{\epsilon}\right)}{\log\left(\dfrac{3e}{2\theta}\right)} \geqslant 1.$$

Then $E \leqslant 3(\frac{2}{3})^m M = 3\epsilon^\alpha M^{1-\alpha}$ where

$$\alpha = \frac{\log(3/2)}{\log(3/2) + \log(e/9)}$$

lies between 0 and 1.

If f is analytic in a larger region we can repeat the process by using new points z_k in a circle of radius $R/4$ about the origin. In those points f is now known with a maximum error E. We can then find the values of f in some points outside the circle of radius $R/4$ etc.

7. Trigonometric Interpolation

For non-analytic functions other types of approximation are often preferable to that by interpolatory polynomials. We mention a formula, due to Bernstein, which gives an approximation to $f(x)$ on $0 \leqslant x \leqslant 1$.

$$P_m(x) = \sum_{k=0}^{m} f\left(\frac{k}{m}\right) \cdot \binom{m}{k} \cdot x^k(1 - x)^{m-k}. \tag{7.1}$$

This is a polynomial of degree m for which

$$\lim_{m\to\infty} P_m(x) = f(x)$$

uniformly if $f(x)$ is continuous.

We shall investigate approximations using trigonometric polynomials determined by f for equidistant values of x. We assume $f(x)$ to have period 2π and define

$$Q_m(x) = \sum_{k=-m}^{m}{}' c_k e^{ikx} \tag{7.2}$$

where

$$\sum_{k=-m}^{m}{}' a_k = \tfrac{1}{2} a_{-m} + \sum_{k=1-m}^{m-1} a_k + \tfrac{1}{2} a_m .$$

We further require that $Q_m(x_k) = f(x_k)$ for

$$x_k = \frac{k\pi}{m} \quad (-m \leqslant k \leqslant m).$$

Since $Q_m(x)$ has period 2π, we have $2m$ conditions for $2m + 1$ coefficients c_k. Our needed additional condition will be $c_{-m} = c_m$ which is not incompatible with the original $2m$ conditions. Moreover

$$\sum_{k=-m}^{m}{}' e^{ilx_k} e^{-ijx_k} = \begin{cases} 0 & \text{if} \quad l \not\equiv j \pmod{2m} \\ 2m & \text{if} \quad l \equiv j \pmod{2m} \end{cases}. \tag{7.3}$$

Thus

$$\sum_k{}' Q_m(x_k)\, e^{-ijx_k} = \sum_l{}' c_l \sum_k{}' e^{ilx_k} e^{-ijx_k}$$

$$= \begin{cases} 2mc_j & \text{for} \quad |j| < m \\ 2m\left(\dfrac{c_m + c_{-m}}{2}\right) = 2mc_m & \text{for} \quad |j| = m\,. \end{cases}$$

This gives

$$c_j = \frac{1}{2m} \sum{}' f(x_k)\, e^{-ijx_k}\,. \tag{7.4}$$

For $m \to \infty$, c_j tends to the fourier coefficient, that is

$$c_j = \frac{1}{2\pi} \sum f(x_k)\, e^{-ijx_k}(x_{k+1} - x_k) \to \frac{1}{2\pi} \int_{-\pi}^{+\pi} f(x)\, e^{-ijx}\, dx.$$

It is clear that $|c_j| \leqslant \text{Max}\,|f|$. We can use this to show that c_j becomes small for large j if f has enough derivatives. For

$$\frac{Q_m\left(x + \dfrac{\pi}{m}\right) - Q_m(x)}{\dfrac{\pi}{m}} = \sum_l{}' c_l e^{ilx} \left(\frac{e^{i(l\pi/m)} - 1}{\dfrac{\pi}{m}}\right).$$

Thus by (7.4)

$$c_l \left(\frac{e^{il\pi/m} - 1}{\dfrac{\pi}{m}}\right) = \frac{1}{2m} \sum{}' \frac{f(x_{k+1}) - f(x_k)}{\dfrac{\pi}{m}}\, e^{-ijx_k}\,.$$

Therefore

$$|c_l| \leqslant \left|\frac{\pi/m}{e^{i(l\pi/m)} - 1}\right| \max|f'| = \frac{\pi/2m}{\sin(\pi l/2m)} \max|f'| \leqslant \frac{\pi}{2l} \max|f'|$$

for $|l| \leqslant m$. Similarly we have for the second derivative $|c_j| \leqslant \pi^2/4l^2 \max|f''|$, or, the "tail end" is majorized by $1/l^2$.

Then for x between x_k and x_{k+1}

$$\begin{aligned}|f(x) - Q_m(x)| &\leqslant |f(x) - f(x_k)| + |f(x_k) - Q_m(x_k)| + |Q_m(x_k) - Q_m(x)| \\ &\leqslant \frac{\pi}{m} \operatorname{Max} |f'| + \frac{\pi}{m} \operatorname{Max} |Q_m'| \\ &\leqslant \frac{\pi}{m} \operatorname{Max} |f'| + \frac{\pi}{m} {\sum_j}' j |c_j| \\ &\leqslant \frac{\pi}{m} \operatorname{Max} |f'| + \frac{2\pi}{m} \sum_{j=1}^{m} \frac{\pi^2}{4j} \operatorname{Max} |f'| \\ &\leqslant \frac{\pi}{m} \operatorname{Max} |f'| + \frac{\pi^3}{2m} (1 + \log m) \operatorname{Max} |f'| .\end{aligned}$$

Hence $Q_m(x) \to f(x)$ uniformly for $f(x)$ of period 2π which are in C^2, that is which have continuous second derivatives.

If we transform the trigonometric formulae for equidistant values of x into a polynomial expression in non-equidistant values of x we obtain an expansion in Chebyshev polynomials.

Let $g(t)$ belong to C^2 for $|t| \leqslant 1$. If $t = \cos x$ and $g(\cos x) = f(x)$, then $f(x)$ belongs to C^2 and is even in x. This implies $c_j = c_{-j}$ so that

$$Q_m(x) = {\sum_l}' c_l \cos (lx) = {\sum_l}' c_l T_l(t) = P_m(t)$$

if $T_l = T_{-l}$. Then P_m is a polynomial of degree m and $P_m(t) = g(t)$ for $t = t_k = \cos k\pi/m$ $(k = 0, 1, \cdots, m)$. Here

$$c_l = \frac{1}{2m} {\sum}' g(t_k) T_l(t_k) .$$

The x_k are the zeros of $\sin mx = 0$ which implies the x_k are the zeros of $\sin x \sin mx = 0$. Then

$$\frac{\cos (m-1) x - \cos (m+1) x}{2} = 0 .$$

In other words, the t_k are the zeros of $T_{m-1}(t) - T_{m+1}(t)$. Moreover $\operatorname{Lim}_{m\to\infty} P_m(t) = g(t)$ since $\operatorname{Lim}_{m\to\infty} Q_m(x) = f(x)$. This proves that for functions f in C^2 the interpolation polynomials converge towards f if they are based on the zeros of $T_{m-1} - T_{m+1}$ instead of on equidistant points.

CHAPTER 5

Solution of Ordinary Differential Equations*

1. The Euler Polygon Method

We shall consider the system of differential equations

$$\frac{dy}{dx} = f(x, y) \tag{1.1a}$$

with the initial conditions

$$y = y^0 \qquad \text{for} \qquad x = z^0 \tag{1.1b}$$

where

$$y = (y_1, y_2, \cdots, y_m) \qquad \text{and} \qquad \frac{dy_i}{dx} = f_i(x, y_1, \cdots, y_m)\,.$$

The first method we shall employ is the polygon method, due to Euler, in which the differential equation is replaced by a difference equation with forward differences. The question to be answered is; does the solution of the difference equation approximate that of the differential equation?

For the sake of convenience, we shall employ equal increments in the independent variable. Then $x_0, x_1, \cdots, x_n$ are related by $x_k = x_0 + kh$. We shall let $y^k = y(x_k)$. We shall solve the difference equation

$$\frac{z^{k+1} - z^k}{h} = f(x_k, z^k) \tag{1.2}$$

with $y^0 = z^0$. In this process we introduce an error in the difference equation in addition to the error in measurement of our quantities.

* See Collatz [4], Hildebrand [19], Antosiewicz and Gautschi [1], Isaacson and Keller [23], Henrici [15], [16].

Therefore we have rather

$$z^{k+1} = z^k + hf(x_k, z^k) + \epsilon^k \tag{1.3}$$

and

$$y^{k+1} = y^k + hf(x_k, y^k) + r^k \tag{1.4}$$

where ϵ^k is the round off error and r^k the truncation error. If we let $\xi^k = z^k - y^k$ we find

$$\xi^{k+1} = \xi^k + h[f(x_k, z^k) - f(x_k, y^k)] - \varepsilon^k - r^k. \tag{1.5}$$

Then $\xi^0 = 0$. We also know

$$r^k = y^{k+1} - y^k - hy'(x_k); \qquad y'(x_k) = f(x_k, y^k) \tag{1.6}$$

so that, by the mean value theorem,

$$r^k = \int_{x_k}^{x_{k+1}} (y'(x) - y'(x_k))\, dx$$

$$= \int_{x_k}^{x_{k+1}} dx \int_{x_k}^{x} y''(\xi)\, d\xi\, .$$

We assume $N(y''(x)) \leqslant Y''$. We can obtain bounds Y'' as follows:

$$y_i'' = \frac{\partial f_i}{\partial x} + \sum_k \frac{\partial f_i}{\partial y_k} \frac{dy_k}{dx}$$

where y_i is the i'th component of y and f_i the i'th component of f. This gives

$$y'' = \frac{\partial f}{\partial x} + Ff$$

where $F = (\partial f_i / \partial y_j)$ and therefore

$$N(y'') \leqslant N\left(\frac{\partial f}{\partial x}\right) + N(F)\, N(f) = Y'' . \tag{1.7}$$

We then have

$$N(r^k) \leqslant N(y'')\frac{h^2}{2} \leqslant \frac{Y''h^2}{2} . \tag{1.8}$$

Moreover,

$$f(x, z^k) - f(x, y^k) = \int_0^1 \frac{d}{dt} f(x, y^k + t\xi^k)\, dt = \int_0^1 F(x, y^k + t\xi^k)\, \xi^k dt\,.$$

We shall assume $N(F(x, \xi)) \leqslant \phi$ and $N(\epsilon^k) \leqslant \epsilon$. We then have

$$N(f(x, z^k) - f(x, y^k)) \leqslant \phi N(\xi^k)$$

so that by (1.5)

$$\begin{aligned} N(\xi^{k+1}) &\leqslant N(\xi^k) + h\phi\, N(\xi^k) + \epsilon + \frac{Y''h^2}{2} \\ &= N(\xi^k)\,[1 + h\phi] + \epsilon + \frac{Y''h^2}{2} \\ &\leqslant N(\xi^k)\, e^{h\phi} + \epsilon + \frac{Y''h^2}{2}\,. \end{aligned}$$

We obtain, by iteration,

$$\begin{aligned} N(\xi^k) &\leqslant \left(\epsilon + \frac{Y''h^2}{2}\right) [1 + e^{h\phi} + \cdots + e^{(k-1)h\phi}] \\ &\leqslant \left(\epsilon + \frac{Y''h^2}{2}\right) (ke^{kh\phi}) \\ &= \left(\frac{\epsilon}{h} + \frac{hY''}{2}\right) [(x_k - x_0)\, e^{\phi(x_k - x_0)}]\,. \end{aligned} \qquad (1.9)$$

The accumulated truncation error tends to 0 like hY'' while the accumulated roundoff error goes to infinity like ϵ/h for $h \to 0$. We thus seek an optimum value for h assuming $\epsilon/h + \frac{1}{2}hY''$ a minimum. That is, we solve

$$\frac{-\epsilon}{h^2} + \tfrac{1}{2}Y'' = 0$$

to find

$$h = \sqrt{\frac{2\epsilon}{Y''}}\,.$$

Then

$$N(\xi^k) \leqslant \sqrt{2\epsilon Y''}\,(x_k - x_0)\, e^{\phi(x_k - x_0)}\,. \qquad (1.10)$$

The convergence holds good as long as bounds ϕ and Y'' can be found, i.e. almost as far as the solution exists.

The above scheme is crude in the sense that more complex schemes give a lower truncation error, that is, one of a higher order of magnitude in h. We shall investigate how to obtain such schemes. For the sake of convenience we shall consider the scalar case since the case of more than one variable goes through in the same way.

2. Refined Difference Schemes

There are different ways of arriving at difference approximations for the derivative which could be used. One way consists of forming the interpolation polynomial $P(x)$ agreeing with y at a number of points x_k, $\cdots$, $x_{k+\nu}$ and then approximating the derivative y' at one of these points, say x_k, by $P'(x_k)$. We have (see (2.12), (2.13), p. 83)

$$P(x) = y_k + \frac{(x - x_k)}{1!} \frac{(y_{k+1} - y_k)}{h}$$

$$+ \frac{(x - x_k)(x - x_{k+1})}{2!} \frac{y_{k+2} - 2y_{k+1} + y_k}{h^2} + \cdots . \tag{1.11}$$

For $\nu = 1$ this leads to

$$P'(x_k) = \frac{y_{k+1} - y_k}{h} \tag{1.12}$$

and suggests the recursion scheme

$$z_{k+1} - z_k = hf(x_k, z_k), \tag{1.13}$$

which is the polygon method.

For $\nu = 2$ we have

$$P'(x_k) = \frac{-y_{k+2} + 4y_{k+1} - 3y_k}{2h}. \tag{1.14}$$

This would suggest the scheme

$$z_{k+2} - 4z_{k+1} + 3z_k = -2hf(x_k, z_k). \tag{1.15}$$

Although this formula has a lower truncation error than the preceeding one it is unstable as will be shown below.

A different approach which produces consistently stable formulas applies the interpolation polynomial to y' rather than to y. One forms the polynomial $Q(x)$ of degree ν which coincides with y' for $x = x_k, \cdots, x_{k+\nu}$ and then integrates this polynomial between the limits $x_{k+\alpha}$ and $x_{k+\beta}$. One obtains an approximate expression for $y_{k+\beta} - y_{k+\alpha}$ in terms of $y'(x_l) = f(x_l, y_l)$ for $l = 0, \cdots, \nu$. For example, if $\nu = 2$, $\alpha = 2$, $\beta = 3$

$$Q(x) = y_k' + \frac{(x - x_k)}{1!} \frac{(y'_{k+1} - y_k')}{h}$$

$$+ \frac{(x - x_k)(x - x_{k+1})}{2!h^2} (y'_{k+2} - 2y'_{k+1} + y_k') = y' + 0(h^3)$$

and then

$$\int_{x_{k+2}}^{x_{k+3}} Q(x) = \frac{h}{12} (5y_k' - 16y'_{k+1} + 23y'_{k+2} = y_{k+3} - y_{k+2} + 0(h^4). \quad (1.16)$$

This leads to the recursion formula

$$z_{k+3} - z_{k+2} = \frac{h}{12} [5f(x_k, z_k) - 16f(x_{k+1}, z_{k+1}) + 23f(x_{k+2}, z_{k+2})]. \quad (1.17)$$

3. Convergence of Difference Approximations

We will consider the convergence of difference schemes for solving the general system of ordinary differential equations:

$$\frac{dy}{dx} = f(x, y); \qquad y(x) = (y_1(x), \cdots, y_m(x))$$

with initial values $y(x_0) = y^0$. We work with an approximate solution vector $z(x) = (z_1(x), \cdots, z_m(x))$. The vector corresponding to $x_n = x_0 + nh$ we call z^n. All previously used recursion formulas are of the following type

$$\sum_{l=0}^{\nu} c_l z^{n+l} = hF(x_n, z^n, \cdots, z^{n+\nu}, h) + \epsilon^n \quad (3.1)$$

where the c_l are constants with $c_\nu = 1$. The expression F is a regular, known function of its arguments and ϵ^n is the round off error. Let $N(\epsilon^n) \leqslant \epsilon$. One assumes that this equation can be solved for $z^{n+\nu}$ (if necessary by an iterative scheme) and thus furnishes all z^n in terms of $z^0, \cdots, z^{\nu-1}$. We define the truncation error r^n by

$$\sum_{l=0}^{\nu} c_l y^{n+l} = hF(x_n, y^n, \cdots, y^{n+\nu}, h) + r^n . \tag{3.2}$$

We assume that there exist constants M and s such that

$$| r^n | < Mh^s$$

for all n. Here we require $s > 1$. We can immediately construct c_l and F so that the round off error is of the proper order of magnitude by requiring that

$$\sum_{l=0}^{\nu} c_l = 0 \qquad \text{and} \qquad F(x, y, \cdots, y, 0) = f(x, y) \cdot \sum_{l=0}^{\nu} lc_l .$$

We associate with the recursion formula the characteristic polynomial

$$P(\lambda) = \sum_{l=0}^{\nu} c_l \lambda^l .$$

It can be seen that a necessary condition for stability of the difference scheme is that all roots of $P(\lambda) = 0$ satisfy $| \lambda | \leqslant 1$. Indeed if $| \lambda | > 1$, for some root λ, this scheme will not be stable even for the simplest differential equation $y' = 0$ In that case $z^n = \xi\lambda^n$ is a solution of $\sum c_l z^{k+l} = 0$ with bounded initial values $z^0, \cdots, z^{\nu-1}$ for any constant vector ξ. For $n \to \infty$ this solution increases exponentially with n. This means that an arbitrarily small initial error can lead to arbitrarily large errors in the result as $h \to 0$. An example is the scheme (1.15).

We assume now that all roots of $P(\lambda) = 0$ are distinct and have $| \lambda | \leqslant 1$. We shall prove that in this case the scheme is stable and converges in the following sense. The total error $N(z^n - y^n)$ is of the order $\epsilon/h + h^{s-1}$. Here it is assumed that the initial errors $z^0 - y^0, \cdots, z^{\nu-1} - y^{\nu-1}$ are of $0(h^{s-1})$.

We shall assume F has derivatives of as many orders as we need.

We want to estimate the error $E^n = z^n - y^n$. We have by the mean value theorem for integrals

$$F(x, z^n, \cdots, z^{n+\nu}, h) - F(x, y^n, \cdots, y^{n+\nu}, h)$$

$$= \int_0^1 \frac{d}{dt} F(x, y^n + t(z^n - y^n), \cdots, y^{n+\nu} + t(z^{n+\nu} - y^{n+\nu}), h)\, dt\,.$$

Considering this last expression componentwise

$$F_i(x, z^n, \cdots, h) - F_i(x, y^n, \cdots, h) = \int_0^1 \sum_{l=0}^{\nu} \sum_{k=1}^{n} \frac{\partial F_i}{\partial y_k^{n+l}} (z_k^{n+l} - y_k^{n+l})\, dt\,.$$

Thus, returning to vector form

$$F(x, z^n, \cdots, h) - F(x, y^n, \cdots, h) = \sum_{l=0}^{\nu} A_l \cdot (z^{n+l} - y^{n+l})$$

where A_l are appropriate matrixes. We then have the Lipschitz condition

$$N[F(x, z^n, \cdots, h) - F(x, y^n, \cdots, h)] \leqslant \sum_{l=0}^{\nu} N(A_l)\, N(z^{n+l} - y^{n+l})\,.$$

Subtracting (3.1), (3.2) yields the following:

$$\sum_{l=0}^{\nu} c_l E^{n+l} = h \sum_{l=0}^{\nu} A_l \cdot E^{n+l} + \epsilon^n - r^n = G^n \qquad (3.3)$$

where

$$E^{n+l} = z^{n+l} - y^{n+l}\,.$$

It remains to find a solution for this inhomogeneous difference equation which may be expressed in terms of the initial conditions and the right hand side only, (Duhamel's principle). We define the scalar function ϕ^n for $n \geqslant 0$ as the fundamental solution of the difference equation if $\sum_{l=0}^{\nu} c_l \phi^{n+l} = 0$ for $n \geqslant 0$, and if $\phi^0 = \phi^1 = \cdots = \phi^{\nu-2} = 0$ and $\phi^{\nu-1} = 1$. We can extend the definition of ϕ^n to all integers n by putting $\phi^n = 0$ for $n < 0$.

Then $\sum_{l=0}^{\nu} c_l \phi^{n+l} = 0$ for $n \neq 1$, and $= 1$ for $n = -1$. We have in complex notation (using $c_\nu = 1$)

$$\phi^n = \frac{1}{2\pi i} \oint_{\mathscr{C}} \frac{\lambda^n}{P(\lambda)} d\lambda \tag{3.4}$$

where the path $\mathscr{C}$ encloses the origin and all the roots of $P(\lambda) = 0$.

Since we assumed all the roots λ_k of $P(\lambda)$ to be distinct, we may evaluate

$$\phi^n = \frac{1}{2\pi i} \oint_{\mathscr{C}} \frac{\lambda^n}{P(\lambda)} d\lambda$$

by the residue theorem. That is for $n \geqslant 0$

$$\phi^n = \sum_{k=1}^{\nu} \frac{\lambda_k^n}{P'(\lambda_k)} \cdot$$

This gives

$$|\phi^n| \leqslant \sum_{k=1}^{\nu} \frac{1}{|P'(\lambda_k)|} = \phi$$

sine all $|\lambda_k| \leqslant 1$.

A special solution of the inhomogeneous equation with the initial values 0 is

$$E^n = \sum_{k \geqslant 0} \phi^{n-k-1} G^k .$$

since then for $n \geqslant 0$

$$\sum_{i=0}^{\nu} c_i E^{n+i} = \sum_{k \geqslant 0} G^k \sum_{i=0}^{\nu} c_i \phi^{n+i-k-1} = G^n .$$

Now any solution of the inhomogeneous equation is given by the general solution of the homogeneous equation plus a special solution of the inhomogeneous equation. Thus

$$E^n = \sum_{k \geqslant 0} \phi^{n-k-1} G^k + \sum_{k=1}^{\nu} \lambda_k^n H^j \tag{3.5}$$

holds for $n \geqslant \nu$.

We want an estimate on E^n. We have the condition on H^k that

$$E^n = \sum_{k=1}^{\nu} \lambda_k{}^n H^k \qquad \text{for} \qquad n = 0, 1, \cdots, \nu - 1 \tag{3.6}$$

and therefore we can determine H^k such that the right hand side of Eq. (3.5) gives the correct solution.

Let $e_n = \max_k N(E^k)$ for $k = 0, \cdots, n$. Then as a first estimate for the G's we have by (3.3)

$$N(G^k) \leqslant h \sum_{l=0}^{\nu} N(A_l)\, N(E^{n+l}) + N(\epsilon^n) + N(r^n)$$

$$\leqslant h \sum_{l=0}^{\nu} N(A_l)\, e_{n+\nu} + \epsilon + Mh^s\,.$$

Let us assume there is an a such that $a \geqslant \sum_{l=0}^{\nu} N(A_l)$. Then

$$N(G^k) \leqslant hae_{n+\nu} + \epsilon + Mh^s\,.$$

Now we want an estimate of the error for the general solution. We first consider $E^n = \sum_{k=1}^{\nu} \lambda_k{}^n H^k$ for $n = 0, 1, \cdots, \nu - 1$ and note that for these $N(E^n) \leqslant e_{\nu-1}$. We then obtain by solving (3.6)

$$N(H^k) \leqslant Le_{\nu-1}$$

where L is a numerical constant depending upon the λ.

We then have from Eq. (3.5)

$$N(E^n) \leqslant n\phi(hae_n + \epsilon + Mh^s) + \nu Le_{\nu-1}$$

since ϕ majorizes the ϕ^n. We now assume that $nh \leqslant X$ or

$$x_n = x_0 + nh \leqslant x_0 + X\,.$$

Therefore

$$N(E^n) \leqslant \phi(Xae_n + n\epsilon + MXh^{s-1}) + \nu Le_{\nu-1}\,.$$

We note that there exists an l such that $e_n = N(E^l)$ with $0 \leqslant l \leqslant n$ and that therefore $e_n = e_l$. Using this, we have

$$N(E^l) = e_n \leqslant \phi(Xae_n + n\epsilon + MXh^{s-1}) + \nu Le_{\nu-1}\,.$$

Therefore, if $\phi Xa < 1$ we have

$$e_n \leqslant \frac{\phi(n\epsilon + Mh^{s-1}X) + \nu L\epsilon_{\nu-1}}{1 - \phi Xa}. \tag{3.7}$$

The condition $X < 1/\phi a$ restricts the size of the interval we must use in order that the estimate be correct.

If all the terms in (3.7) are of the order h^{s-1}, that is, if

$$e_{\nu-1} \leqslant bh^{s-1} \qquad \text{(initial error)} \tag{3.8a}$$

$$n\epsilon \leqslant ch^{s-1} \qquad \text{(round off error)} \tag{3.8b}$$

then the total error would be of the same order as the accumulated truncation error. That is

$$N(E^n) \leqslant dh^{s-1}. \tag{3.9}$$

We can use the Taylors series to obtain our values for $z^0, \cdots, z^{\nu-1}$ in order to insure $y^k - z^k = 0(h^{s-1})$; $0 \leqslant k \leqslant \nu - 1$. Since we can determine any derivative of y^0 from $y' = f(x, y)$ we can compute:

$$y^1 = y^0 + hy'^0 + \frac{h^2}{2} y''^0 + \cdots + \frac{h^{s-2}}{(s-2)!} y^{s-2}{}_0 + 0(h^{s-1}).$$

We let

$$z^1 = y^0 + hy'^0 + \frac{h}{2} y''^0 + \cdots + \frac{h^{s-2}}{(s-2)!} y^{s-2}{}_0$$

and, proceeding in a similar manner, determine $z^2, \cdots, z^{\nu-1}$. For the stable situation the accumulated round off error is at most proportional to the number of steps. For given h we have to keep the individual error so small that (3.8b) holds for $n \leqslant X/h$. Thus, if all the proper conditions are satisfied, and the z^k are chosen as above, then for the interval X the error will be less than or equal to a constant multiplied by h^{s-1}. We can continue the solution further out, obtaining another interval $x_0 + X \leqslant x \leqslant x_0 + 2X$ abutting on the original one. Then $X_0' = X_0 + nh$ or $X_0' + nh = X_0''$. In this case the initial error is again of order h^{s-1} and the total error will still be of order h^{s-1} although there may be a worsening of the constant d. It should be noted that all these estimates require that the initial error be of the order of h^{s-1}.

There is a device which may be used to improve the order of approximation. Consider $y' = f(x, y)$; $y(x_0) = y_0$ where y is now a scalar. The recursion formula in the simplest case goes over into (taking subscripts for scalars as opposed to superscripts for vectors)

$$z_{n+1} = z_n + hf(x_n, z_n) + \epsilon_n$$

$$y_{n+1} = y_n + hf(x_n, y_n) + r_n .$$

Then

$$\begin{aligned} r_n &= y_{n+1} - y_n - hy_n' \\ &= y_n + hy_n' + \frac{h^2}{2} y_n'' + 0(h^3) - y_n - hy_n' \\ &= \frac{h^2}{2} y_n'' + 0(h^3) . \end{aligned}$$

Now

$$E_n = z_n - y_n;$$

$$E_{n+1} = E_n + hf_y(x_n, y_n + \theta E_n)E_n + \epsilon_n - \frac{h^2}{2} y_n'' + 0(h^3) .$$

We wish to compare this with the solution of the auxilliary differential equation

$$\xi'(x) = f_y(x, y)\, \xi - \tfrac{1}{2} y''; \qquad \xi(x_0) = 0.$$

We claim that, approximately,

$$E_n = h\xi(x_n) + \cdots .$$

Now

$$\xi_{n+1} = \xi_n + hf_y(x, y_n)\, \xi_n - \tfrac{1}{2} hy_n'' + 0(h^2)$$

and

$$h\xi_{n+1} = h\xi_n + h(h\xi_n) f_y(x, y) - \tfrac{1}{2} h^2 y_n'' + 0(h^3) .$$

Let $\eta_n = E_n - h\xi_n$. Then

$$\eta_{n+1} = \eta_n + f_y(x_n, y_n)\,(h\eta_n) + 0(hE_n^2) + 0(h^3 + \epsilon).$$

Applying the estimate (3.7) with $s = 2$ and $e_{\nu-1} = 0$ gives $E_n = 0(n\epsilon + h)$ if there is no initial error. Therefore,

$$\eta_{n+1} = \eta_n + f_y(x_n, y_n) h\eta_n + 0(h^3 + h^2 n\epsilon + hn^2\epsilon^2 + \epsilon)$$

and

$$| \eta_n | = 0(nh^3 + hn^3\epsilon^2 + n\epsilon) .$$

Since $nh < X$ this gives

$$\eta_n = 0(Xh^2 + X^3h^{-2}\epsilon^2 + Xh^{-1}\epsilon) .$$

From this it follows that

$$\begin{aligned} z_n &= y_n + E_n \\ &= y(x_n) + h\xi(x_n) + 0(Xh^2 + X^3h^{-2}\epsilon^2 + Xh^{-1}\epsilon) \end{aligned}$$

where ξ is the solution of the auxilliary differential equation.

If we allow a superscript to the left to indicate mesh width we have

$$\begin{aligned} {}^h z_n &= y_n + h\xi_n + 0(h^2X + \cdots) \\ {}^{2h} z_n &= y_n + 2h\xi_n + 0(h^2X + \cdots) . \end{aligned}$$

Therefore

$$w_n = 2\,{}^h z_n - {}^{2h} z_n = y_n + 0(Xh^2 + X^3h^{-2}\epsilon^2 + Xh^{-1}\epsilon) .$$

We have therefore gained one order of magnitude in the accumulated truncation error by using the original difference formula for two different mesh sizes to compute w_n.

CHAPTER 6

The Heat Equation*

1. The Appropriate Problems

The numerical solution of Partial Differential Equations is a very complex field which has not been completely explored. With Ordinary Differential Equations the considerations were fairly straightforward and the primary object was to achieve better schemes, that is, schemes which give more rapid convergence. In the case of Partial Differential Equations we shall have as our primary concern the finding of a numerical solution rather than its improvement.

We shall be concerned in the beginning with examples of Partial Differential Equations of the second order. The first cases we shall consider are those wherein the coefficients are constant since similar considerations will have to be used for variable coefficients.

Our first investigation shall concern itself with the one dimensional equation for heat conduction, i.e., in proper units,

$$\frac{\partial u}{\partial t} = \frac{\partial^2 u}{\partial x^2}; \qquad t > 0\,. \tag{1.1}$$

The natural problem which is suggested for the temperature u has the following data: The initial state is prescribed for a given region on the x-axis, that is, $u(x, 0) = f(x)$; $a \leqslant x \leqslant b$; and, if boundaries are present conditions are prescribed there. Say in the case of a bar of length $b - a$ lying on the x axis we would require that $u(a, t)$ and $u(b, t)$ are prescribed for all $t \geqslant 0$. Other conditions

* See Douglas and Rachford [10], John [24], Richtmyer [35], Forsythe and Wasow [11]. For a general discussion of stability for difference schemes see also Lax and Richtmyer [28], and Lax [27].

may occur. For exemple, if we consider the ends of the bar as insulated we have $u_x(a, t) = 0$ and $u_x(b, t) = 0$ as a mathematical expression of this fact.

2. Exact Solution of the Initial Value Problem

We shall first consider $a = -\infty$ and $b = +\infty$. In this case there are no boundary conditions. We still have $u(x, 0) = f(x)$; $-\infty < x < \infty$. If $f(x)$ is continuous and bounded we have the following analytic solution of $u_t = u_{xx}$

$$u(x, t) = \int_{-\infty}^{+\infty} \frac{e^{-\xi^2/4t}}{\sqrt{4\pi t}} f(x + \xi)\, d\xi \,. \tag{2.1}$$

This may be written as

$$u(x, t) = \int_{-\infty}^{+\infty} \frac{e^{-(\xi-x)^2/4t}}{\sqrt{4\pi t}} f(\xi)\, d\xi \,. \tag{2.2}$$

The kernel of this integral,

$$K(\xi, x, t) = \frac{e^{-(\xi-x)^2/4t}}{\sqrt{4\pi t}} \tag{2.3}$$

is a solution of the Partial Differential Equation depending upon the parameter ξ. We have

$$\lim_{t\to 0} \frac{e^{-(\xi-x)^2/4t}}{\sqrt{4\pi t}} = 0 \qquad \text{for} \qquad x \neq \xi$$

and

$$\lim_{t\to 0} \frac{e^{-(\xi-x)^2/4t}}{\sqrt{4\pi t}} = \infty \qquad \text{for} \qquad x = \xi \,.$$

This suggests that we might use the Dirac δ-function for our initial condition;

$$K(x, 0) = \delta(x - \xi). \qquad \int_{-\infty}^{+\infty} K(x, 0)\, dx = 1. \tag{2.4}$$

We can also find the solution (2.1) using Fourier transformations. Let

$$f(x) = \int e^{iax} \phi(a) \, da \,. \tag{2.5}$$

For explicit initial values e^{iax} the solution of the equation would be $e^{iax-a^2 t}$. This would give

$$u(x, t) = \int e^{iax-a^2 t} \phi(a) \, da \,. \tag{2.6}$$

We have from the Fourier formula

$$\phi(\alpha) = \frac{1}{2\pi} \int e^{-i\alpha\xi} f(\xi) \, d\xi \,. \tag{2.7}$$

Thus

$$u(x, t) = \int_{-\infty}^{+\infty} f(\xi) \, d\xi \int_{-\infty}^{+\infty} \frac{e^{ia(x-\xi)-a^2 t}}{2\pi} \, da \,. \tag{2.8}$$

Now $\int_{-\infty}^{+\infty} [e^{ia(x-\xi)-a^2 t}/2\pi] \, da$ may be evaluated explicitly by reduction to $\int_{-\infty}^{+\infty} e^{-a^2} \, da = \sqrt{\pi}$; it is found to be $K(\xi, x, t)$. The solution is unique if $u(x, t)$ is bounded for $t \geqslant 0$ and all x.

3. Difference Approximations

For numerical solution we shall go to the simplest possible difference equation bearing in mind that the formula

$$u(x, t) = \int_{-\infty}^{\infty} \frac{e^{-(\xi-x)^2/4t}}{\sqrt{4\pi t}} f(\xi) \, d\xi$$

shows our solution depends upon the initial values *everywhere*. That is, the difference scheme must eventually take into account all the points on the initial line.

We shall cover the entire plane with a rectangular grid composed of a set of equidistant lines of distance h apart parallel to the t

axis and a set of equidistant lines of distance k apart parallel to the x-axis wherein one of the first set coincides with the t-axis and one of the second set coincides with the x-axis. Thus the points of intersection of these lines shall have coordinates $x = lh$, $t = jk$ where l and j are integers.

Now we shall construct our difference equation from the Partial Differential Equation using central differences in x. That is

$$\frac{v(x, t + k) - v(x, t)}{h} = \frac{v(x - h, t) - 2v(x, t) + v(x + h, t)}{h^2} . \tag{3.1}$$

This formula connects v in four points on the grid which form the vertices and midpoint of the base of an isoceles triangle with base lying on one of the lines parallel to the x-axis. It is easy to see that forward differences in the x direction would not lead to an approximate solution since only points to one side fo the point in question would contribute to the difference scheme and we have seen that the entire initial line must be accounted for in a solution.

We solve for $v(x, t + k)$ and obtain

$$v(x, t + k) = \lambda v(x + h, t) + (1 - 2\lambda)\, v(x, t) + \lambda v(x - h, t) \tag{3.2}$$

where $\lambda = k/h^2$. Geometrical observations delineate the *domain of dependence* of a point (x, t) as the segment $[x - (h/k)\, t, x + (h/k)\, t]$ on the initial line.

A scheme in which the mesh refinement leads to an approximation must eventually use initial values on an everywhere dense set of the whole initial line. Thus in the limit we must have $k/h \to 0$ in order that enough points be used on the x-axis.

In practice we have in our recursion scheme a round-off error $\epsilon(x, t)$ and we evaluate v only at points of the grid. Therefore

$$\begin{aligned} v(lh, (j + 1)\, k) = \lambda v((l + 1)\, h, jk) + (1 - 2\lambda)\, v(lh, jk) \\ + \lambda v((l - 1)\, h, jk) + \epsilon_{l,j} \, . \end{aligned} \tag{3.3}$$

Using $v(lh, 0) = f(lh)$ as our initial values we solve this difference equation.

4. Error Estimate Stability Condition

The question arises as to how well the solution of $u_t = u_{xx}$ satisfies the difference equations. Let

$$u(lh, (j+1)k) = \lambda u((l+1)h, jk) + (1-2\lambda)\, u(lh, jk) + \lambda u((l-1)h, jk) + r_{l,j}\,.$$

We shall estimate $r_{l,j}$ using Taylors theorem. Thus

$$\begin{aligned} r_{l,j} &= k\,\frac{u(lh,(j+1)k) - u(lh, jk)}{k} - k\,\frac{u((l-1)h, jk) - 2u(lh, jk) + u((l+1)h, jk)}{h^2} \\ &= k\left(u_t + \frac{k}{2}\,\overline{\overline{u_{tt}}}\right) + k\left(-u_{xx} - \frac{h^2}{12}\,\overline{u_{xxxx}}\right) \\ &= k^2\left(\frac{1}{2}\,\overline{\overline{u_{tt}}} - \frac{1}{12\lambda}\,\overline{u_{xxxx}}\right) \\ &= \frac{k^2}{2}\left(\overline{\overline{u}}_{xxxx} - \frac{1}{6\lambda}\,\overline{u}_{xxxx}\right) \end{aligned} \tag{4.1}$$

where the bars indicate appropriate intermediate values of the variables.

For the particular case $\lambda = \frac{1}{6}$ the truncation error will be at least of third order in k.

We now note that the solution u of the heat equation satisfies the maximum principle:

$$|\, u(x, t)\,| \leqslant \underset{\xi}{\text{l.u.b.}}\, |\, f(\xi)\,|\,.$$

This follows from Eq. (2.1) since

$$|\, u(x, t)\,| \leqslant \underset{x}{\text{l.u.b.}}\, |\, f(x)\,| \int_{-\infty}^{\infty} \frac{e^{-\xi^2/4t}}{\sqrt{4\pi t}}\, d\xi = \underset{x}{\text{l.u.b.}}\, |\, f(x)\,|\,.$$

Since u_{xxxx} is also a solution of the heat equation with initial values $f^{IV}(x)$ we find that

$$|\, u_{xxxx}\,| \leqslant \text{l.u.b.}\, |\, f^{IV}(x)\,| = F_4\,.$$

Thus

$$| r_{l,j} | \leqslant \frac{k^2}{2}\left(1 + \frac{1}{6\lambda}\right) F_4 . \tag{4.2}$$

We assume $| \epsilon_{l,j} | \leqslant \epsilon$. We define the error $E_{l,j}$ as

$$E_{l,j} = v(lh, jk) - u(lh, jk)$$

and have therefore

$$E_{l,j+1} = \lambda E_{l-1,j} + (1 - 2\lambda) E_{l,j} + \lambda E_{l+1,j} + \epsilon_{l,j} - r_{l,j} .$$

We have $E_{l,0} = 0$ since $v(x, 0) = f(x)$.

We shall now estimate our error. Let

$$E_j = \operatorname*{Max}_{-\infty < l < +\infty} | E_{l,j} |;$$

thus $E_0 = 0$. Now

$$E_{j+1} \leqslant (| \lambda | + | 1 - 2\lambda | + | \lambda |) E_j + \epsilon + \frac{k^2}{2}\left(1 + \frac{1}{6\lambda}\right) F_4 .$$

If here $\lambda \leqslant \frac{1}{2}$ then $1 - 2\lambda \geqslant 0$ and

$$E_{j+1} \leqslant E_j + \epsilon + \frac{k^2}{2}\left(1 + \frac{1}{6\lambda}\right) F_4 .$$

Thus by iteration of this formula for $t = jk$

$$| v(x, t) - u(x, t) | \leqslant E_j \leqslant j\epsilon + \frac{k^2}{2} j \left(1 + \frac{1}{6\lambda}\right) F_4$$

$$= \frac{t}{k}\epsilon + \frac{tk}{2}\left(1 + \frac{1}{6\lambda}\right) \text{l.u.b.} | f^{IV}(\xi) | . \tag{4.3}$$

We see then that a sufficient condition for convergence of v to u in the absence of round off error is that h and k tend to zero in such a manner that $\lambda = k/h^2$ has a fixed value with $0 < \lambda \leqslant \frac{1}{2}$, and that $f^{IV}(x)$ exists and is bounded. If individual round off errors are present but do not exceed the value ϵ then the "accumulated round off error" can be estimated by $j\epsilon$ where j is the number of steps taken in the t direction. Of course this error might tend to ∞ as j goes to ∞. We call the scheme *stable* if its exact solution converges for all sufficiently often differentiable data. This is seen to be the case for $\lambda \leqslant \frac{1}{2}$. At the same time we notice that the "accumulated round off error" goes only as a reciprocal power of the mesh size; $j = t/k$. This is an example of the general phenomenon that stability in the sense of convergence implies also a certain degree of stability under small disturbances.

5. Divergence in the Unstable Case

We shall now establish that $\lambda \leqslant \frac{1}{2}$ is also necessary for stability (at least if $\lambda = k/h^2$ is held fixed). For this purpose we construct an $f(x)$ for which we will have divergence for $\lambda > \frac{1}{2}$.

We consider an exponential solution $w(x, t) = e^{iax-\beta t}$ of the difference equation. That is, for

$$w(x, t + k) = \lambda w(x - h, t) + (1 - 2\lambda)\, w(x, t) + \lambda w(x + h, t).$$

This gives

$$\begin{aligned} e^{-\beta k} &= \lambda e^{-iah} + (1 - 2\lambda) + \lambda e^{iah} \\ &= 1 - 4\lambda \sin^2 \frac{ah}{2}. \end{aligned} \tag{5.1}$$

Thus

$$w(x, t) = e^{iax} \left(1 - 4\lambda \sin^2 \frac{ah}{2}\right)^{t/k} \tag{5.2}$$

and

$$w(x, 0) = e^{iax}.$$

It follows that, for $\lambda \leqslant \frac{1}{2}$, $|w| \leqslant 1$ for all t. On the other hand, for $\lambda > \frac{1}{2}$, for certain a we would have $|1 - 4\lambda \sin^2 ah/2| > 1$ and thus $|w|$ will be very large if t/k is large enough. We shall now produce a concrete instance of divergence. Let

$$f(x) = \sum_{s=0}^{\infty} \exp\,[-3^s] \cos(\pi 2^s x)$$

which is an entire analytic function.

Then

$$w(x, t) = \sum_{s=0}^{\infty} \exp[-3^s] \cos(\pi 2^s x) \left[1 - 4\lambda \sin^2\left(\frac{\pi 2^s h}{2}\right)\right]^{t/k}.$$

We shall assume for simplicity that $\frac{1}{2} < \lambda < 1$ and $k/h^2 = \lambda$ is fixed. Let $h = 1/2^m$ then $k = \lambda/2^{2m}$. Thus the value of $| w(0,t) |$ gives

$$| w(0, t) | = \sum_{s=0}^{\infty} e^{-3^s}(1 - 4\lambda \sin^2 2^{s-m-1}\pi)^{t/k} |$$

$$\geqslant - \sum_{t=m+1}^{\infty} e^{-3^s} + e^{-3^m} | 1 - 4\lambda |^{t/k} - \sum_{s=0}^{m-1} e^{-3^s}.$$

Now $(4\lambda - 1) = | 1 - 4\lambda | > 1$. Thus

$$w(0, t) \geqslant - \sum_{0}^{\infty} e^{-3^s} + \exp\left[\frac{t}{\lambda} 4^m \log(4\lambda - 1) - 3^m\right]$$

tends to ∞ as $m \to \infty$, that is as $h \to 0$. (The assumption that λ is fixed and less than 1 is not essential; it only matters that λ is bounded away from $\frac{1}{2}$.)

6. Acceleration Schemes

A more exact calculation of the truncation error $r(x, t)$ leads to "acceleration schemes" similar to those considered on p. 104. By (4.1)

$$r(x, t) = \frac{k^2}{2} u_{tt} - \frac{kh^2}{12} u_{xxxx} + 0(k^3)$$

$$= \left(\frac{k^2}{2} - \frac{kh^2}{12}\right) u_{xxxx} + 0(k^3).$$

We define the operator Ω by

$$\Omega g(x) = \lambda g(x - h) + (1 - 2\lambda) g(x) + \lambda g(x + h). \quad (6.1)$$

Consequently we have for $E(x, t) = v(x, t) - u(x, t)$ by (3.3)

$$E(x, t + k) = \Omega E(x, t) - \left(\frac{k^2}{2} - \frac{kh^2}{12}\right) u_{xxxx} + 0(k^3) + 0(\epsilon) .$$

We can calculate E by solving the following differential equation

$$w_t = w_{xx} + u_{xxxx}$$

where we take $w(x, 0) = 0$. For the solution of the differential equation we have by (4.1)

$$w(x, t + k) - \Omega w(x, t) = ku_{xxxx} + 0(k^2 w_{tt} + kh^2 w_{xxxx}) .$$

Therefore

$$E(x, t + k) + \left(\frac{k}{2} - \frac{h^2}{12}\right) w(x, t + k)$$

$$= \Omega \left[E(x, t) + \left(\frac{k}{2} - \frac{h^2}{12}\right) w(x, t)\right] + 0(\epsilon + k^3) .$$

We shall assume that $v(x, 0) = f(x)$ and thus $E(x, 0) = 0$. Therefore [see (4.3)]

$$E(x, t) + \left(\frac{k}{2} - \frac{h^2}{12}\right) w(x, t) = 0(j\epsilon + jk^3) = 0(j\epsilon + tk^2) .$$

Since $v(x, t) = u(x, t) + E(x, t)$ we have

$$v(x, t) = u(x, t) - \left(\frac{k}{2} - \frac{h^2}{12}\right) w(x, t) + 0(j\epsilon + tk^2) .$$

We shall consider two different mesh widths corresponding to the same λ, namely (1) (h, k) and (2) $(2h, 4k)$. This leaves only h to observe since k is λh^2 and λ is fixed. Now

$$v(x, t, 2h, 4k) = u(x, t) - 4 \left(\frac{k}{2} - \frac{h^2}{12}\right) w(x, t) + 0(j\epsilon + tk^2) .$$

Therefore

$$4v(x, t, h, k) - v(x, t, 2h, 4k) = 3u(x, t) + 0(j\epsilon + tk^2) .$$

Thus $\frac{4}{3} v(x, t, h, k) - \frac{1}{3} v(x, t, 2h, 4k)$ is a much better approximation insofar as the accumulated truncation error is concerned.

7. Relaxation of the Regularity Assumptions

We saw that $f(x) \in C^4$ implies the solution of the difference equation converges uniformly to the solution of the Partial Differential Equation.

We shall show that if $f(x)$ is only uniformly continuous we still have convergence. In fact, if $f(x)$ can be approximated uniformly by functions $f_n(x) \in C^4$ and $| f_n^{IV}(x) | < k_n$ then, as we shall show,

$$\lim_{n,k\to 0} | v(x, t, h, k) - u(x, t) | = 0$$

uniformly.

Let the expression $v_n(x, t, h, k)$ be the solution of the difference scheme of mesh (h, k) which has $v_n(x, 0, h, k) = f_n(x)$. Now we have

$$\begin{aligned} | v(x, t, h, k) - u(x, t) | \leqslant & \; | v(x, t, h, k) - v_n(x, t, h, k) | \\ & + | v_n(x, t, h, k) - u_n(x, t) | \\ & + | u_n(x, t) - u(x, t) | \end{aligned}$$

where $u_n(x, t)$ is the solution of the differential equation with initial conditions $u(x, 0) = f_n(x)$.

Now for $\lambda \leqslant \frac{1}{2}$ the difference equation obeys by (4.3) the same maximum principle as the differential equation. Thus, since the $f_n(x)$ approximate $f(x)$ uniformly, we may choose an $n_0(\delta)$ such that for $n \geqslant n_0(\delta)$ we shall have $| f_n(x) - f(x) | \leqslant \delta$. Then also

$$| u_{n_0}(x, t) - u(x, t) | \leqslant \delta, \qquad | v_{n_0}(x, t, h, k) - v(x, t, h, k) | \leqslant \delta.$$

Moreover, for (h, k) small enough depending on δ and n_0 we have

$$| v_{n_0}(x, t, h, k) - u_{n_0}(x, t) | \leqslant \delta .$$

These two results together with the maximum principle give us $| v(x, t, h, k) - u(x, t) | \leqslant 3\delta$ for $\lambda \leqslant \frac{1}{2}$ and h and k sufficiently small. Therefore the difference scheme converges.

What sort of functions $f(x)$ con be approximated in this way? Well, if $f(x)$ is uniformly continuous for the infinite interval and uniformly bounded then we can produce suitable $f_n(x)$ as follows:

We make use of the solution to the heat equation

$$u(x, t) = \int_{-\infty}^{+\infty} \frac{e^{-(x-\xi)^2/4t}}{\sqrt{4\pi t}} f(\xi)\, d\xi \, .$$

Now if $f(\xi)$ is uniformly continuous and bounded then $u(x, t)$ is analytic in x for $t > 0$. This gives the existence of u_{xxxx} and moreover that u_{xxxx} is bounded for all x and $\operatorname{Lim}_{t\to 0} u(x, t) = f(x)$ uniformly in x. Now if we define $f_n(x) = u(x, 1/n)$ then certainly $\operatorname{Lim}_{n\to\infty} f_n(x) = f(x)$ uniformly in x.

8. Probabilistic Interpretation of the Difference Scheme

We have in the notation of (6.1) the difference equation $v(x, t + k) = \Omega v(x, t)$ and $v(x, 0) = f(x)$. It is easily seen that $v(x, jk)$ is of the form

$$v(x, jk) = \sum_{l} f(x + lh)\, c_{l,j} \tag{8.1}$$

where $c_{l,j} = 0$ for $|\, l \,| > j$ and $c_{l,j} = c_{-l,j}$. Now let $x = ih$ and consider that special $f(x)$ such that

$$f(x) = \begin{Bmatrix} 0;\ x \neq 0 \\ 1;\ x = 0 \end{Bmatrix} . \tag{8.2}$$

It follows immediately that $v(ih, jk) = c_{-i,j} = c_{i,j}$. Thus $c_{i,j}$ is the special solution where $f(x)$ is as defined above. In particular we have

$$c_{l,j+1} = \lambda c_{l-1,j} + (1 - 2\lambda)\, c_{l,j} + \lambda c_{l+1,j} \, .$$

It is possible to give an interpretation of the $c_{l,j}$ utilizing probability theory as follows: (Assume that $\lambda \leqslant \frac{1}{2}$).

We permit a particle to be at any of the places $x = 0, \pm h, \pm 2h, \cdots$. The particle may be at different places at different times. If the particle is at ih at time t then the probabilities of its being at $(i - 1)\, h$, $2h$, and $(i + 1)\, h$ at time $t + k$ shall be respectively λ, $1 - 2\lambda$ and λ.

Now if $v(x, t)$ is the probability that the particle is at place x at time t, then clearly $v(x, t + k) = \Omega v(x, t)$.

Thus $c_{l,j}$ is the probability that the particle is at place $x = lh$ at time $t = jk$ assuming that it started at $x = 0$ at time $t = 0$.

9. Asymptotic Expansion of the Fundamental Solution of the Difference Scheme by the Method of Stationary Phase*

We can also obtain an integral representation of the $c_{l,j}$ using the fact that exponential solutions are present. Now $f(x) = e^{i\alpha x}$ implies that v is a solution of the difference equation of the form $v(x, t) = e^{i\alpha x - \beta t}$. We require

$$v(x, t + k) = e^{-\beta k} v(x, t) = \Omega v(x, t) .$$

Here

$$\Omega v(x, t) = (\lambda e^{-i\alpha h} + (1 - 2\lambda) + \lambda e^{-i\alpha h})\, v(x, t)$$

$$= \left(1 - 4\lambda \sin^2 \frac{\alpha h}{2}\right) v(x, t) .$$

Therefore again, as in (5.1), (5.2),

$$e^{-\beta k} = 1 - 4\lambda \sin^2 \left(\frac{\alpha h}{2}\right)$$

and, by (8.1),

$$v(x, t) = e^{i\alpha x - \beta jk} = \left(1 - 4\lambda \sin^2 \frac{\alpha h}{2}\right)^j e^{i\alpha x}$$

$$= \sum_l c_{l,j} e^{il\alpha h} e^{i\alpha x} .$$

Letting $\alpha h = \theta$ we find as a necessary condition: the identity

$$\left(1 - 4\lambda \sin^2 \frac{\theta}{2}\right)^j = \sum c_{l,j} c^{il\theta}$$

must hold for all θ.

* See John [24].

Now this sum is a (finite) Fourier series and thus

$$c_{l,j} = \frac{1}{2\pi} \int_{-\pi}^{+\pi} \left(1 - 4\lambda \sin^2 \frac{\theta}{2}\right)^j e^{-il\theta} \, d\theta \, .$$

Out of this we shall obtain asymptotic expressions for $c_{l,j}$ for large j and $| l | \leqslant j$. We shall find that if $\lambda < \frac{1}{2}$ then, up to terms of higher order,

$$c_{l,j} = \frac{e^{-l^2/4\lambda j}}{\sqrt{4\pi\lambda j}} + 0\left(\frac{1}{j^{3/2}}\right)$$

which will enable us to prove convergence for bounded Rieman integrable $f(x)$.

Let us now assume $\lambda < \frac{1}{2}$. Then we have

$$\left| 1 - 4\lambda \sin^2 \frac{z}{2} \right| \leqslant 1 \qquad \text{for} \qquad \text{all real } z.$$

Introduce the function $f(z)$ by

$$I = 1 - 4\lambda \sin^2 \frac{z}{2} = e^{-f(z)} \qquad \text{for} \qquad -\pi \leqslant z \leqslant \pi \, .$$

Then $I = 1$ for $z = 0$ and $f(z) > 0$ for $0 < z \leqslant \pi$. For small real z, I is positive and analytic and therefore $f(z)$ is analytic and representable by

$$f(z) = - \log \left(1 - 4\lambda \sin^2 \frac{z}{2} \right) = \lambda z^2 + cz^4 + dz^6 + \cdots$$

as a power series expansion. Now there exists an $M > 0$ such that $f(z)/z^2 \geqslant M$; $| z | \leqslant \pi$; and therefore $e^{-f(z)} \leqslant e^{-Mz^2}$. Let us write $c_{l,j}$ as

$$c_{l,j} = \frac{1}{2\pi} \int_{|z| \leqslant \epsilon} \left(1 - 4\lambda \sin^2 \frac{z}{2}\right)^j e^{ilz} \, dz$$

$$+ \frac{1}{2\pi} \int_{\epsilon \leqslant |z| \leqslant \pi} \left(1 - 4\lambda \sin^2 \frac{z}{2}\right)^j e^{ilz} \, dz \, .$$

Now

$$\left| \frac{1}{2\pi} \int_{\epsilon \leqslant |z| \leqslant \pi} \left(1 - 4\lambda \sin^2 \frac{z}{2}\right)^j e^{ilz} \, dz \right| \leqslant \frac{2}{2\pi} \int_{\epsilon}^{\infty} e^{-Mjz^2} \, dz$$

$$\leqslant \frac{1}{\pi} \int_{\epsilon}^{\infty} \frac{z}{\epsilon} e^{-Mjz^2} \, dz = \frac{1}{2\pi\epsilon Mj} e^{-Mj\epsilon^2} .$$

Thus

$$c_{l,j} = \frac{1}{2\pi} \int_{-\epsilon}^{\epsilon} e^{-jf(z)-ilz} \, dz + 0\left(\frac{1}{\epsilon j} e^{-Mj\epsilon^2}\right) .$$

Now we wish to replace $f(z)$ by the first term in its power series and must therefore calculate the error introduced. Since

$$f(z) = \lambda z^2 + 0(z^4)$$

we have

$$c_{l,j} = \frac{1}{2\pi} \int_{-\epsilon}^{\epsilon} e^{-\lambda jz^2-ilz} e^{0(jz^4)} \, dz + 0\left(\frac{1}{\epsilon j} e^{-Mj\epsilon^2}\right) .$$

We require that $| jz^4 | \leqslant 1$ for $-\epsilon \leqslant z \leqslant \epsilon$ which will be achieved if we use $j\epsilon^4 = 1$ as definition of ϵ. Thus $j\epsilon^2 = \sqrt{j}$ and $e^{0(jz^4)} = 1 + 0(jz^4)$ since the exponent is bounded. Thus

$$c_{l,j} = \frac{1}{2\pi} \int_{-\epsilon}^{+\epsilon} e^{-\lambda jz^2-ilz} \, dz + 0\left(\frac{1}{2\pi} \int_{-\infty}^{\infty} e^{-\lambda jz^2} jz^4 dz + \frac{1}{j^{3/4}} e^{-M\sqrt{j}}\right)$$

$$= \frac{1}{2\pi} \int_{-\epsilon}^{+\epsilon} e^{-\lambda jz^2-ilz} + 0\left(\frac{1}{j^{3/2}} + \frac{1}{j^{3/4}} e^{-M\sqrt{j}}\right) .$$

Now if we let the limits of integration be $-\infty$ and $+\infty$ instead of $-\epsilon$ and $+\epsilon$ we shall introduce a further error $0(j^{-3/4} e^{-\lambda\sqrt{2}})$ and thus

$$c_{l,j} = \frac{1}{2\pi} \int_{-\infty}^{+\infty} e^{-\lambda jz^2-ilz} \, dz + 0\left[\frac{1}{j^{3/2}} + \frac{1}{j^{3/4}} (e^{-M\sqrt{j}} + e^{-\lambda\sqrt{j}})\right] .$$

Now

$$\int_{-\infty}^{\infty} e^{-\lambda jz^2-ilz} \, dz = \int_{-\infty}^{+\infty} e^{-\lambda j[z+(il/2\lambda j)]^2-(l^2/4\lambda j)} \, dz .$$

Let $\zeta = z + il/2\lambda j$. Then we have

$$\int_{-\infty}^{\infty} e^{-\lambda j z^2 - ilz}\, dz = \int_{-\infty}^{\infty} e^{-\lambda j \zeta^2 - (l^2/4\lambda j)}\, d\zeta = \frac{\sqrt{\pi}}{\sqrt{\lambda j}}\, e^{-(l^2/4\lambda j)}$$

since the limits of integration are not affected. Finally therefore

$$c_{l,j} = \frac{1}{\sqrt{4\pi\lambda j}}\, e^{-(l^2/4\lambda j)} + 0\left(\frac{1}{j^{3/2}}\right). \tag{9.1}$$

10. Convergence of the Difference Scheme for Riemann Integrable and Bounded Data

Now the solution of the difference scheme is given by

$$v(x, jk) = \sum_{|l| \leqslant j} c_{l,j} f(x + lh).$$

Assume $|f(x)| \leqslant F$. Then the solution of the difference scheme by (9.1) is

$$v(x, t) = v(x, jk) = \sum_{|l| \leqslant j} \frac{e^{-(l^2/4\lambda j)}}{\sqrt{4\pi\lambda j}} f(x + lh) + 0\left(\frac{F}{j^{1/2}}\right).$$

Here $0(F/j^{1/2}) \to 0$ as $j \to \infty$. Let $lh = \xi_l$. Then

$$v(x, jk) = \sum_{\substack{|\xi| \leqslant jh \\ (jh = t/\lambda h)}} \frac{e^{-(\xi_l^2/4t)}}{\sqrt{4\pi t}} f(x + \xi_l)\, \Delta\xi_l + 0\left(\frac{F}{\sqrt{j}}\right).$$

Let us assume $f(x)$ is Rieman integrable in every finite interval. We then find

$$v(x, t) = \sum_{|\xi_l| \leqslant A} \frac{e^{-(\xi_l^2/4t)}}{\sqrt{4\pi t}} f(x + \xi_l)\, \Delta\xi_l + 0\left(\frac{\sqrt{t}}{A}\, e^{-A^2/t} + \frac{h}{\sqrt{t}}\right) F.$$

Now let $h \to 0$. For $h \leqslant \delta(\epsilon, A, t)$ we have

$$v(x, t) = \int_{-A}^{A} \frac{e^{-(\xi^2/4t)}}{\sqrt{4\pi t}} f(x + \xi)\, d\xi \pm \epsilon + 0\left(\frac{\sqrt{t}}{A}\, e^{-A^2/t} + \frac{h}{\sqrt{t}}\right) F.$$

Now if we choose A large enough then

$$v(x, t) = \int_{-\infty}^{\infty} \frac{e^{-(\xi^2/4t)}}{\sqrt{4\pi t}} f(x + \xi)\, d\xi \pm 3\epsilon .$$

Thus $|\, v(x, t) - u(x, t) \,| \leqslant 3\epsilon$ for h sufficiently small if $\lambda < \frac{1}{2}$ and $f(x)$ is Riemann integrable and uniformly bounded.

11. The Mixed Initial-Boundary-Value Problem

We have heretofore considered the heat equation with the initial conditions prescribed along the entire x-axis. Now we go over to the case where the initial values $u = f(x)$ are given in the closed interval $0 \leqslant x \leqslant L$ and, moreover, boundary conditions $u = g(t)$ and $u = h(t)$ for $x = 0$ and $x = L$ are prescribed. The problem is to determine $u(x, t)$ inside the strip A bounded by $x = 0$, $x = L$ and the x-axis from 0 to L. For the numerical solution we shall construct a difference scheme which converges to a solution of the partial differential equation.

Cover A by a rectangular grid with mesh width $h = L/n$ in the x direction and k in the t direction. We assume $v = f(x)$ to be our initial values for the difference equation, while the values at the points $(0, nk)$ and (L, lk) coincide with the boundary values there. Then, permitting a 'round off' error ϵ, we use the difference equation

$$v(x, t + k) = \lambda v(x + h, t) + (1 - 2\lambda)\, v(x, t) + \lambda v(x - h, t) + \epsilon(x, t)$$

for $0 < x < L$, while using the exact boundary conditions for $x = 0, L$.

As before, we have

$$u(x, t + k) = \lambda u(x + h, t) + (1 - 2\lambda)\, u(x, t) - \lambda u(x - h, t) + r(x, t)$$

and we define

$$E(x, t) = v(x, t) - u(x, t) .$$

This gives

$$E(x, t + k) = \lambda E(x + h, t) + (1 - 2\lambda)\, E(x, t) + \lambda E(x - h, t) + \epsilon(x, t) - r(x, t)$$

and

$$E(x, 0) = 0, \qquad E(0, t) = 0 \qquad \text{and} \qquad E(L, t) = 0\,.$$

If we have a solution $u \in C^4$ we can estimate r easily finding $r = 0(k^2)$ for $\lambda \leqslant \frac{1}{2}$ [See (4.1)]. Assume $|\,\epsilon(x, t)\,| \leqslant \epsilon$. Then

$$|\,E(x, t + k)\,| \leqslant \operatorname*{Max}_x |\,E(x, t)\,| + \epsilon + 0(k^2)\,.$$

Thus we still have a maximum principle

$$\operatorname*{Max}_x |\,E\,|\,x, t + k)\,| \leqslant \operatorname*{Max}_x |\,E(x, t)\,| + \epsilon + 0(k^2)\,.$$

Using this principle repeatedly we find

$$|\,E(x, t)\,| \leqslant 0 + \frac{t}{k}(\epsilon + 0(k^2)) \leqslant \frac{t}{k}\epsilon + 0(tk)$$

where $t\epsilon/k$ represents the accumulated round off error which might go to ∞ as k goes to zero while $0(tk)$, the accumulated truncation error, goes to zero as $k \to \infty$. An optimum value for k could be easily determined.

We have assumed $u \in C^4$. This can only hold if the data for u satisfy certain compatibility conditions in the corners, including

$$g(0) = f(0); \qquad h(0) = f(L); \qquad g'(0) = f''(0) \qquad \text{etc.}$$

We may however get rid of most of these conditions by utilizing functions approximating f, g and h which do "fit together" sufficiently well. For if $f_n \overset{\text{unif.}}{\to} f$; $g_n \overset{\text{unif.}}{\to} g$; and $h_n \overset{\text{unif.}}{\to} h$, we have that $u_n \to u$ and $v_n \to v$ (at least if round off errors are disregarded). This follows from the maximum principle as follows: for $0 < x < L$

$$|\,v(x, t + k)\,| \leqslant \operatorname*{Max}_x |\,v(x, t)\,|\,,$$

while for $x = 0$

$$|\,v(x, t + k)\,| \leqslant \operatorname{Max} |\,g(t)\,|\,,$$

and for $x = L$

$$|\,v(x, t + k)\,| \leqslant \operatorname{Max} |\,h(t)\,|\,.$$

Therefore

$$\operatorname{Max} |\,v(x, t + k)\,| \leqslant \operatorname{Max}\,(|\,v(x, t)\,|, |\,g(t)\,|, |\,h(t)\,|)\,.$$

From this we can iterate and obtain

$$\text{Max} \mid v(x, t) \mid \leqslant \text{Max} \, (\mid f \mid, \mid h \mid, \mid g \mid) \, .$$

Therefore, in particular,

$$\mid v_n - v_m \mid \leqslant \text{Max} \, (\mid f_n - f_m \mid, \mid g_n - g_m \mid, \mid h_n - h_m \mid) \, .$$

For $h \to 0$ it follows that also

$$\mid u_n - u_m \mid \leqslant \text{Max} \, (\mid f_n - f_m \mid, \mid g_n - g_m \mid, \mid h_n - h_m \mid) \, .$$

Let us assume $f_n \to f$, $g_n \to g$, $h_n \to h$ uniformly. Then $u_n \to u$ uniformly. The limit u will be a 'weak' solution of the differential equation if f, g and $h \in C^0$. We note that the solution does not depend upon the precise choice of the approximating functions f_n, g_n and h_n since for fixed h and k $v_n(x, t, h, k) \to v(x, t, h, k)$ and

$$\begin{aligned} \mid u(x, t) - v(x, t, h, k) \mid \leqslant & \mid v(x, t, h, k) - v_n(x, t, h, k) \mid \\ & + \mid v_n(x, t, h, k) - u_n(x, t) \mid \\ & + \mid u_n(x, t) - u(x, t) \mid \, . \end{aligned}$$

We take n so large that $\mid v - v_n \mid < \epsilon$ and $\mid u_n - u \mid < \epsilon$ and then choose h, k small enough such that $\mid v_n - u_n \mid < \epsilon$. This can all be done since the data f_n, g_n, h_n are smooth and fit together. Therefore

$$\mid u(x, t) - v(x, t, h, k \mid < 3\epsilon \qquad \text{for} \qquad h, k \text{ small enough.}$$

This shows: the solution of the difference scheme converges to the solution of the differential equation whenever the data are uniformly approximated by nice consistent functions. We note that any continuous f, g, h which satisfy $f(0) = g(0)$, $f(L) = h(0)$ can be approximated in the desired fashion, and hence constitute data for which the solution of the difference equation will approximate the solution of the differential equation.

We can even consider the case where the data f, g, and $h \in C^0$ but do not fit at all at the corners say $g = 0$, $h = 0$. and $f = 1$. We shall define a new solution u^* satisfying the following: $u^*(0, t) = g(t)$; $u^*(L, t) = h(t)$ and $u^*(x, 0) = f^*(x)$ where $f^*(0) = g(0)$; $f^*(L) = h(0)$ and $f^*(x) \in C^0$. Now $w = u - u^*$

satisfies the differential equation and the conditions. $w = 0$ on the side of A and $w = f - f^*$ at the bottom. Thus it is sufficient to consider the case where $g = 0$, $h = 0$ and $u(x, 0) = \phi(x)$.

In order to show that the difference scheme converges we shall use the reflection principle to reduce our situation to the case where the initial data are given on the entire x-axis. We note that $u = 0$ along the t-axis; u may be continued as an odd function of x which still satisfies the differential equation. The differential equation is preserved if we replace x by $-x$. Moreover, for $u(-x, t) = -u(x, t)$ we have

$$u(+0, t) = -u(-0, t) = 0\,, \qquad u_x(+0, t) = u_x(-0, t)\,,$$
$$u_{xx}(+0, t) = u_t(+0, t) = 0 = u_{xx}(-0, t)\,.$$

Thus the first and second x derivatives are continuous. Similarly, u can be continued across the line $x = L$ by the equation

$$u(2L - x, t) = -u(x, t)\,.$$

Continuing the initial function $\phi(x)$ in the same manner, we see that u is a solution of a pure initial problem with $u(x, 0)$ prescribed for all x. Since the resulting $\phi(x)$ is continuous at all but a countable number of points $\phi(x)$ is Riemann integrable and the difference scheme converges by what was proved before. Thus no compatibility condition in the corners is needed at all for convergence of the solution of the difference equation.

12. An Implicit Scheme for the Heat Equation

Heretofore we have only considered 'explicit' difference schemes in which $u(x, t + k)$ is expressed in terms of the values of u at the time t and of boundary data. We now replace the differential equation $u_x - u_{xx} = w(x, t)$ by the difference equation

$$\begin{aligned} L(v) &= \frac{v(x, t) - v(x, t - k)}{k} - \frac{v(x - h, t) - 2v(x, t) + v(x + h, t)}{h^2} \\ &= w(x, t) \end{aligned} \tag{12.1}$$

for $0 < x < L$. In addition, we again require $u(x, 0) = f(x)$, $u(0, t) = g(t)$, $u(L, t) = h(t)$. In order to find v at time t once the values at the time $t - k$ are known entails the solution of a whole system of linear equations, and hence more work than in an explicit scheme. This disadvantage is balanced, as we shall see, by bigher stability of the implicit scheme which permits the use of larger steps in the t direction.

For the determination of v for a given t and $0 \leqslant x \leqslant L$, we have the system of as many equations as unknowns, namely the two boundary conditions for $x = 0, L$ and the difference equation for $0 < x < L$.

We shall establish a maximum principal for this difference equation. In order to do this we solve for $v(x, t)$

$$v(x, t) = \frac{\lambda}{1 + 2\lambda}\{v(x + h, t) + v(x - h, t)\} + \frac{1}{1 + 2\lambda} v(x, t - k) + \frac{k}{1 - 2\lambda} w(x, t) \qquad (12.2)$$

where $\lambda = k/h^2$. We assume

$$| w(x, t) | \leqslant W, \qquad | f(x) | \leqslant F; \qquad | g(t) | \leqslant G; \qquad | h(t) | \leqslant H$$

and

$$\underset{0 \leqslant x \leqslant L}{\text{Max}} | v(x, t) | = V_t .$$

This gives for $0 < x < L$

$$| v(x, t) | \leqslant \frac{2\lambda}{1 + 2\lambda} V_t + \frac{1}{1 + 2\lambda} V_{t-k} + \frac{k}{1 + 2\lambda} W.$$

The exclusion of $(0, t)$ and (L, t) leads to two cases.

Case I: $(v(x, t))$ assumes, for fixed t, its maximum value inside of the interval, whence

$$V_t \leqslant \frac{2\lambda}{1 + 2\lambda} V_t + \frac{1}{1 + 2\lambda} V_{t-k} + \frac{k}{1 + 2\lambda} W.$$

This gives

$$V_t \leqslant V_{t-k} + kW.$$

Case II: $| v(x, t) |$, for fixed t, assumes its maximum value for $x = 0$ or $x = L$. This gives $V_t \leqslant \text{Max}\,(G, H)$.

In both cases

$$V_t \leqslant \text{Max}\,(V_{t-k}, G, H) + kW. \tag{12.3}$$

This shows that the system of linear equations can be solved since it permits us to prove the fact that the system of homogeneous equations (corresponding to $G = H = V_{t-k} = W = 0$) has only the trivial solution.

We have from (12.3) for $t = jk$

$$\begin{aligned} V_t &\leqslant \text{Max}\,(V_{t-k}, G, H) + kW \\ &\leqslant \text{Max}\,(V_{t-2k}, G, H) + 2kW \\ &\;\;\vdots \qquad\qquad \vdots \\ &\leqslant \text{Max}\,(F, G, H) + jkW \end{aligned}$$

since $V_0 = F$. Thus

$$|\, v(x, t)\,| \leqslant V_t \leqslant \text{Max}\,(F, G, H) + tW\,. \tag{12.4}$$

We shall use this to show the convergence of the difference scheme.

The error for $w = 0$ is given by

$$E(x, t) = v(x, t) - u(x, t)$$

where u is the solution of $u_t = u_{xx}$ and v is the solution of the difference equation

$$v(x, t) = \frac{\lambda}{1 + 2\lambda}[v(x - h, t) + v(x + h, t)] + \frac{1}{1 + 2\lambda} v(x, t - k) + \epsilon(x, t)\,.$$

Here $\epsilon(x, t)$ is the round off error. Let $|\,\epsilon(x, t)\,| \leqslant \epsilon$. Thus

$$|\, L[v]\,| \leqslant \left| (1 + 2\lambda)\frac{\epsilon(x, t)}{k} \right| \leqslant \left| \frac{1 + 2\lambda}{k} \right| \epsilon\,.$$

Moreover, we have for the truncation error for $u \in C^4$

$$L[u] = 0(k + h^2)\,.$$

This in turn gives

$$|\, L[E]\,| \leqslant \frac{1 + 2\lambda}{k}\epsilon + 0(k + h^2) = W\,.$$

E satisfies homogeneous boundary conditions at $v = 0, L$ and $t = 0$. Hence from (12.4)

$$| E(x, t) | = t \left[\frac{1 + 2\lambda}{k} \epsilon + 0(k + h^2)\right].$$

If $\epsilon = 0$ convergence is clear since $0(k + h^2) \to 0$ as k and $h \to 0$ in any manner whatever. The accumulated round off error is less than or equal to

$$\frac{t}{k}(1 + 2\lambda) \epsilon = j(1 + 2\lambda) \epsilon .$$

13. Method of Solution of the Difference Equation for the Implicit Scheme

It remains to discuss how to solve the system of linear equations (12.2) at each step (we assume that $w = 0$ and that no round off error is committed). The simplest method (which applies also to dimensions greater than one) is to iterate: assuming $v(x, t - k)$ has been determined we take $v^0(x, t) = v(x, t - k)$, $v^{n+1}(0, t) = g$, $v^{n+1}(L, t) = h$, while for $0 < x < L$

$$v^{n+1}(x, t) = \frac{\lambda}{1 + 2\lambda}[v^n(x - h, t) + v^n(x + h, t)] + \frac{1}{1 + 2\lambda} v(x, t - k)$$

Then for $0 < x < L$

$$v^{n+1}(x, t) - v^n(x, t) = \frac{\lambda}{1 + 2\lambda}[v^n(x - h, t) - v^{n-1}(x - h, t)$$
$$+ v^n(x + h, t) - v^{n-1}(x + h, t)] .$$

Therefore for $0 \leqslant x \leqslant L$

$$\text{Max} | v^{n+1} - v^n | \leqslant \frac{2\lambda}{1 + 2\lambda} \text{Max} | v^n - v^{n-1} |$$

and by iteration

$$\text{Max} | v^{n+1} - v^n | \leqslant \left(\frac{2\lambda}{1 + 2\lambda}\right)^n | v^1 - v^0 | .$$

Thus v^n converges geometrically with ratio $2\lambda/(1 + 2\lambda) < 1$ towards the solution $v(x, t)$.

Another method, which, incidentally, works only for dimension one, consists in reducing the "boundary value problem" for the determination of $v(x, t)$ to "initial value problems". We make use of three auxiliary functions w_1, w_2 and w_3 such that

$$
\begin{array}{llll}
M[w_1] = 0 & w_1 = 1 & \text{for} & x = 0 \\
 & w_1 = 0 & \text{for} & x = h \\
M[w_2] = 0 & w_2 = 0 & \text{for} & x = 0 \\
 & w_2 = 1 & \text{for} & x = h
\end{array}
$$

$$M[w_3] = \frac{1}{1 + 2\lambda} v(x, t - k)$$

$$
\begin{array}{lll}
w_3 = 0 & \text{for} & x = 0 \\
w_3 = 0 & \text{for} & h = 0 .
\end{array}
$$

where the operator M acting on $w = w(x) = w(lh)$ is defined by

$$M(w) = w(x) - \frac{\lambda}{1 + 2\lambda} [w(x - h) + w(x + h)]$$

we can find w_1, w_2 and w_3 recursively. Let $v = \alpha w_1 + \beta w_2 + w_3$; α and β can be determined from $\alpha = g(t)$ and

$$\alpha w_1(L) + \beta w_2(L) + w_3(L) = h(t).$$

The linear equation for β can be solved since $w_2(L) \neq 0$. This is satisfied, for if $w_2(L) = 0$ the solution $w_2(x)$ would vanish at $x = 0$ and $x = L$ and therefore due to the maximum principle would vanish identically contrary to $w_2(h) = 1$.

CHAPTER 7

The Wave Equation

1. Analytic Solution. The Simplest Difference Scheme*

We consider now the wave equation in one dimension $u_{xx} = u_{tt}$. This will serve as the simplest example of a *hyperbolic* equation. Assume the initial conditions to be $u(x, 0) = f(x)$ and $u_t(x, 0) = g(x)$. We have an explicit solution for this problem

$$u(x, t) = \frac{f(x+t) + f(x-t)}{2} + \tfrac{1}{2}\int_{x-t}^{x+t} g(\xi)\, d\xi\,. \tag{1.1}$$

Of prime importance is the question of how the solution depends upon the initial data. We obtain this information by considering the characteristics of the equation, which, in this case, since the waves propagate with velocity one, are straight lines through (x, t) with slopes 1 and -1. These lines intersect the x-axis at points $(x - t, 0)$ and $(x + t, 0)$. $u(x, t)$ depends on the initial data in this interval.

We define

$$L[v] = \frac{v(x, t+k) - 2v(x, t) + v(x, t-k)}{k^2} - \frac{v(x+h, t) - 2v(x, t) + v(x-h, t)}{h^2} = 0\,. \tag{1.2}$$

Here we assume for the time being that there is no round off error. It is clear that if we know v at $(x, t - k)$, $(x + h, t)$, $(x - h, t)$ and (x, t) we can determine v at $(x, t + k)$. This shows if we know v for two different adjacent values of t we can compute it for the

* See Courant, Friedrichs, and Lewy [6].

subsequent value of t. Thus for initial values for the difference equation it is sufficient to know v for $t = 0$ and $t = k$. We could take for example $v(x, 0) = f(x)$ and $v(x, k) = f(x) + kg$. This is theoretically possible, but involves a large truncation error. However, we can utilize u_t in a different way by choosing initial values of v such that

$$\frac{v(x, k) - v(x, -k)}{2k} = g(x) \tag{1.3}$$

and $v(x, 0) = f(x)$ and $L[v] = 0$ for $t = 0$. This gives

$$v(x, -k) = v(x, k) - 2kg(x)\,.$$

From $L[v] = 0$ for $t = 0$ we have

$$\frac{v(x, k) - 2f(x) + v(x, k) - 2kg(x)}{k^2} = \frac{f(x-h) - 2f(x) + f(x+h)}{h^2}$$

which leads to

$$v(x, k) = f(x) + \frac{k^2}{2h^2}\,[f(x-h) - 2f(x) + f(x+h)] + kg(x)\,.$$

Thus this formulation of the initial conditions gives the required value of $v(x, k)$ and $v(x, 0)$. From this we can proceed with our difference scheme and need only to investigate convergence. The first consideration is that the difference scheme uses the proper domain of dependence. We define $\lambda = k/h$. Obviously this leads to a domain of dependence for $v(x, t)$ on the initial values in the interval from $x - t/\lambda$ to $x + t/\lambda$. Thus, unlesss $\lambda \leqslant 1$ the entire proper domain of dependence for u will not be taken into account and hence one cannot expect to obtain the correct solution. It turns out that $\lambda \leqslant 1$ is a sufficient condition for convergence for all smooth functions as initial values, whereas we can construct a function for which the scheme does not converge for $\lambda > 1$. Convergence is harder to prove than in the case of the heat equation since there is no maximum principle due to the appearance of $- v(x, t - k)$ in the difference equation (1.2) which can be written

$$\begin{aligned} v(x, t + k) = \lambda^2 v(x - h, t) + \lambda^2 v(x + h, t) + 2(1 - \lambda^2)\, v(x, t) \\ - v(x, t - k)\,. \end{aligned} \tag{1.4}$$

It should ne noted, however, that for dimension one the differential equation has the simple bound (which does not hold for higher dimensions) for its solution

$$| u(x, t) | \leqslant \text{Max} | f(x) | + t \,\text{Max} | g(x) | .$$

2. Exponential Solution of the Difference Equation

We consider a special solution of the form $v(x, t) = e^{i\alpha x + i\beta t}$. Putting this into $L[v]$ we have

$$e^{i\alpha x+i\beta t}\left[-\frac{4}{k^2}\sin^2\frac{\beta k}{2}\right] + e^{i\alpha x+i\beta t}\left[\frac{4}{h^2}\sin^2\frac{\alpha h}{2}\right] = 0$$

or

$$\sin^2\frac{\beta k}{2} = \lambda^2 \sin^2\frac{\alpha h}{2}$$

where α is an arbitrary real number. There are two values of $e^{i\beta k}$ which satisfy this equation. Then, since β is real for $0 \leqslant \lambda \leqslant 1$ we have $| v | = 1$. If $\lambda > 1$ then β for a certain real α will have negative imaginary part and thus there will exist a solution bounded for $t = 0$ which grows exponentially, namely

$$v(x, t) = e^{i\alpha x}(e^{i\beta k})^{t/k} .$$

3. Convergence Proof by Fourier Transformation*

Since it is difficult to obtain an exact estimate from the difference equation directly we use Fourier transformations. The case we consider is

$$f(x) = e^{i\alpha x}; \qquad g(x) = 0 .$$

Then, using the initial conditions in the form (1.3),

$$v(x, t) = e^{i\alpha x}\cos\beta t$$

where we define β as the smallest positive value for which

$$\sin\frac{\beta k}{2} = \frac{k}{h}\sin\frac{\alpha h}{2} .$$

* See H. Lewy [1].

If we consider in addition the case $f(x) = 0$ and $g(x) = e^{i\alpha x}$ we find similarly using (1.2) that

$$v(x, t) = e^{i\alpha x}k \frac{\sin \beta t}{\sin \beta k} .$$

As h and $k \to 0$ regardless of λ we find $\beta \to \alpha$ for fixed α so that the exponential solutions of the difference equation converge to exponential solutions of the differential equation. The question we consider is: does the same conclusion hold for general $f(x)$ and $g(x)$ when we build up a solution by superposition of exponentials? We have for $h \to 0\alpha$

$$\sin \frac{\beta k}{2} = \frac{\alpha k}{2} + 0(\alpha^3 h^2 k)$$

and thus

$$\frac{\beta k}{2} = \frac{\alpha k}{2} + 0(\alpha^3 h^2 k)$$

uniformly for $| \alpha | \leqslant A$. Therefore

$$\beta = \alpha + 0(\alpha^3 h^2) .$$

We have $t = jk$ where we tacitly assume $| t | \leqslant T$. We conclude

$$\begin{aligned} \cos \beta t = \cos \beta jk &= \cos [\alpha kj + 0(\alpha^3 h^2 kj)] \\ &= \cos [\alpha t + 0(\alpha^3 h^2 t)] \to \cos \alpha t \qquad \text{as} \qquad h \to 0 \end{aligned}$$

and moreover the convergence is uniform for $| \alpha | \leqslant A$ and $| t | \leqslant T$. Then also uniformly for bounded α and t

$$e^{i\alpha x} \cos \beta t \to e^{i\alpha x} \cos \alpha \qquad \text{for} \qquad h \to 0$$

and

$$e^{i\alpha x}k \frac{\sin \beta t}{\sin \beta k} \to e^{i\alpha x} \frac{\sin \alpha t}{\alpha} \qquad \text{for} \qquad h \to 0 .$$

Let us consider data f, g represented by a Fourier integral. That is

$$g(x) = \frac{1}{\sqrt{2\pi}} \int_{-\infty}^{\infty} e^{i\alpha x} \psi(x) \, d\alpha$$

and

$$f(x) = \frac{1}{\sqrt{2\pi}} \int_{-\infty}^{\infty} e^{i\alpha x} \phi(\alpha) \, d\alpha .$$

We also assume that the integrals for f and g converge absolutely. The solution of the difference equation is then

$$v(x, t) = \frac{1}{\sqrt{2\pi}} \int_{-\infty}^{\infty} e^{i\alpha x} \left(\cos \beta t\, \phi(\alpha) + k \frac{\sin \beta t}{\sin \beta k} \psi(\alpha)\right) d\alpha . \tag{2.1}$$

As a *stability condition* we assume $k/h = \lambda \leqslant 1$. This results in $\cos \beta t$ and $k(\sin \beta t/\sin \beta k)$ being bounded. Namely, β is real for $\lambda \leqslant 1$, therefore $|\cos \beta t| \leqslant 1$ and

$$\left| k \frac{\sin \beta t}{\sin \beta k} \right| = \left| k \frac{\sin \beta kj}{\sin \beta k} \right| \leqslant kj = t$$

where j is an integer.

We next wish to show the convergence of the integral as $h \to 0$. We write [ ] for the integrand in (2.1) and have

$$\int_{-\infty}^{\infty} [\,]\, d\alpha = \int_{-A}^{A} [\,]\, d\alpha + \int_{A}^{\infty} [\,]\, d\alpha + \int_{-\infty}^{-A} [\,]\, d\alpha .$$

We can choose A large enough such that $|\int_A^\infty [\,]\, d\alpha| \leqslant \epsilon$ and $|\int_{-\infty}^{-A} [\,]\, d\alpha \leqslant \epsilon$ since $\int |\phi|\, d\alpha$ and $\int |\psi|\, d\alpha$ converge. Let h and k be so small that

$$\left| \int_{-A}^{A} e^{i\alpha x} \left(\cos \beta t\, \phi(\alpha) + k \frac{\sin \beta t}{\sin \beta k} \psi(\alpha)\right) dx \right.$$
$$\left. - \int_{-A}^{A} e^{i\alpha x} \left(\cos \alpha t\, \phi(\alpha) + \frac{\sin \alpha t}{\alpha} \psi(\alpha)\right) d\alpha \right| \leqslant \epsilon .$$

Then

$$\int_{-\infty}^{\infty} e^{i\alpha x} \left(\cos \beta t\, \phi(x) + k \frac{\sin \beta t}{\sin \beta k} \psi(\alpha)\right) d\alpha$$
$$= \int_{-\infty}^{\infty} e^{i\alpha x} \left(\cos \alpha t\, \phi(\alpha) + \frac{\sin \alpha t}{\alpha} \psi(\alpha)\right) d\alpha \pm 5\epsilon.$$

Therefore for $|t| \leqslant T$

$$v(x, t) \rightarrow u(x, t) \text{ uniformly}$$

if the initial data have an absolutely convergent Fourier integral. This condition is satisfied when f and g are twice continuously differentiable. [We can always assume that f and g vanish outside a finite interval, since the domain of dependence for the difference equation is bounded].

We have heretofore assumed a precise solution at each step. However, we cannot represent the round off error in the form of a Fourier integral.

4. Convergence in the Unstable Case for Analytic Data*

We note that the scheme might converge even in the non-stable case if the data were nice enough, for example, if the Fourier transforms ψ and ϕ die out fast enough at ∞.

In this direction we have a theorem due to Dahlquist:

If $f(x)$ and $g(x)$ are analytic for complex $|x| \leqslant R$ then we have convergence for sufficiently small $|x|$, $|t|$ regardless of the stability conditions.

For simplicity let $g(x) = 0$. Analyticity of f implies that

$$f(x) = \frac{1}{2\pi i} \int_{|\zeta|=R} \frac{f(\zeta)}{\zeta - x} \, d\zeta \qquad \text{for} \qquad |x| < R.$$

If Re $(\zeta - x) > 0$ then

$$\frac{1}{\zeta - x} = \int_0^\infty e^{-(\zeta - x)\alpha} \, d\alpha \, .$$

Consider the circle $|\zeta| = R$ divided into four sections by the lines Re $(\zeta) = \pm$ Im (ζ). There is one sector for which Re$(\zeta - x) > 0$ for all ζ on it and for $|x| < R/10$. Then the above integral serves for this sector to represent $1/(\zeta - x)$. Similar expressions exist for the other sectors. For example, for that sector in which $Im(\zeta - x) > 0$ we have

$$\frac{1}{\zeta - x} = -i \int_0^\infty e^{+i(\zeta - x)\alpha} \, d\alpha \, .$$

Now the solution of the difference equation corresponds to the sum of the contributions to f from each sector.

The contribution of a point ζ in the first sector to the solution of the initial value problem is

$$f(\zeta) \int_0^\infty e^{-(\zeta - x)\alpha} \cosh \beta t \, d\alpha$$

* See Dahlquist [8], John [25].

where

$$\sinh \frac{\beta k}{2} = \frac{k}{h} \sinh \frac{\alpha h}{2} .$$

Now β is real if we assume α is real. Moreover, for fixed k/h the ratio β/α is bounded. Thus there exists an M such that $| \cosh \beta t | \leqslant e^{M\alpha t}$. Therefore the contribution of ζ is at most

$$f(\zeta) \int_0^\infty e^{-(\zeta - x)\alpha + M\alpha t} \, d\alpha$$

and for t so small that $Mt < \text{Re}\,(\zeta - x)$ the integral converges since the integrand is $\leqslant 1$. Moreover, for bounded α the exponential expression converges for $h \to 0$ to a solution of the wave equation. We now note that the same procedure may be followed in the other three sectors. Thus we have that the solution of the difference scheme corresponding to analytic initial data converges to a solution of the differential equation.

5. L_2-Estimates for the Solution of the Difference Scheme

Returning to the general initial value problem where f and g have Fourier transforms and $\lambda \leqslant 1$ we may draw useful information from Parseval's theorem which yields on the basis of (2.1)

$$\sqrt{\int_{-\infty}^{\infty} | v(x\ \ t) |^2 \, dx} = \sqrt{\int_{-\infty}^{\infty} \left| \cos \beta t \, \phi(\alpha) + k \frac{\sin \beta t}{\sin \beta k} \psi(\alpha) \right|^2 d\alpha} \, .$$

This implies that

$$\sqrt{\int_{-\infty}^{\infty} | v(x, t) |^2 \, dx} \leqslant \sqrt{\int_{-\infty}^{\infty} | \cos \beta t \, \phi(\alpha) |^2 \, d\alpha} + \sqrt{\int_{-\infty}^{\infty} \left| k \frac{\sin \beta t}{\sin \beta k} \psi(\alpha) \right|^2 d\alpha}$$

$$\leqslant \sqrt{\int_{-\infty}^{\infty} | \phi(\alpha) |^2 \, d\alpha} + t \sqrt{\int_{-\infty}^{\infty} | \psi(\alpha) |^2 \, d\alpha}$$

$$= \sqrt{\int_{-\infty}^{\infty} f(x)^2 \, dx} + t \sqrt{\int_{-\infty}^{\infty} g(x)^2 \, dx} \, . \tag{5.1}$$

The aboslute value signs may be removed from the $v(x, t)$ as long as we deal with real valued functions. There are no convergence difficulties for these improper integrals. We can always assume that $f(x)$ and $g(x) = 0$ for large enough $|x|$ since the values outside the domain of dependence are non-contributory to the solution).

The bad feature of this is that we require integration and we may only know $f(x)$ at the lattice points. In order to utilize this method when f and g are known only at lattice points we make the following extension: for $f(x)$ take $f(lh)$ for $lh - h/2 < x < lh + h/2$ and for $g(x)$ take $g(lh)$ for $lh - h/2 < x < lh + h/2$. Now if the initial data are step functions of this character so is the solution $v(x, t)$ for all t:

$$v(x, t) = v(lh, t) \quad \text{for} \quad \left(lh - \frac{h}{2} < x < lh + \frac{h}{2}\right).$$

Then from the above integral inequality (5.1) there follows the analogous inequality for v at discrete points

$$\sqrt{\sum_l v(lh, t)^2} \leqslant \sqrt{\sum_l f(lh)^2} + t\sqrt{\sum_l g(lh)^2}\,.$$

Consider $|f(x)| \leqslant F$ and $|g(x)| \leqslant G$. Then

$$v(x, t) \leqslant \sqrt{\sum_l v(lh, t)^2} \leqslant \sqrt{2j+1}\,(F + tG) \tag{5.2}$$

for j steps in the t direction since we may drop all l such that lh is outside the domain of dependence.

6. Estimates of Accumulated Round Off Error

We now sketch the method for getting the accumulated round off error. We first consider the effect of a single error on the solution at a later stage and then utilize superposition. The recursion formula for v shall be [see (1.4)]

$$v(x, t+k) = 2v(x, t) - v(x, t-k) + \lambda^2 v(x+h, t) - \lambda^2 2v(x, t) + \lambda^2 v(x-h, t) + \epsilon(x, t)\,.$$

We assume that $\epsilon(x, t) = 0$ except at $t = 0$, where $|\epsilon(x, 0)| \leqslant \epsilon$. Now $v(x, t)$ comes out to be the same if we also require $\epsilon(x, 0) = 0$ but change the values of the initial data suitably. We leave $f(x)$ unchanged but replace

$$g(x) \text{ by } g(x) + \epsilon(x, 0)/2k \text{ so that}$$

(see (1.3))

$$\frac{v(x, k) - v(x, -k)}{2k} = g(x) + \frac{\epsilon(x, t)}{2k}.$$

The total effect of this error at time t is by (5.2) $\leqslant (t\sqrt{2j + 1})/2k)\epsilon \leqslant \epsilon j^{3/2}$. If we now commit errors $\leqslant \epsilon$ at all places, then all points in the domain of dependence of a point (x, t) contribute, and the total accumulated round off error is of the order $j\epsilon j^{3/2} = \epsilon j^{3/2}$ considering the rectangle containing the point (x, t) and its domain of dependence. The same methods apply to the solution of the wave equation in three dimensions.

CHAPTER 8

Friedrich's Method for Symmetric Hyperbolic Systems*

1. Example of the One-Dimensional Wave Equation

We can reduce the wave equation $u_{xx} = u_{tt}$ to a symmetric system of first order equations. Put $u_t = p$ and $u_x = q$. Then we have $p_t = q_x$ and $q_t = p_x$. It is advantageous to use matrix notation

$$\begin{pmatrix} p \\ q \end{pmatrix} = U \qquad \text{and} \qquad U_t = \begin{pmatrix} 0 & \dfrac{\delta}{\partial x} \\ \dfrac{\partial}{\partial x} & 0 \end{pmatrix} U . \tag{1.1}$$

The initial conditions are

$$U = \begin{pmatrix} g(x) \\ f'(x) \end{pmatrix} = F(x) \qquad \text{for} \qquad t = 0 .$$

We wish to replace this by a difference scheme. One way would be to replace the first differential equation by

$$\frac{p(x, t + k) - p(x, t)}{k} = \frac{q(x + h, t) - q(x, t)}{h}$$

and similarly for the second one. This is no good since it utilizes initial data only on one side of x and therefore cannot take the entire domain of dependence into account, A second possible scheme would be

$$\frac{p(x, t + k) - p(x, t)}{k} = \frac{q(x + h, t) - q(x - h, t)}{2h}$$

* See Friedrichs [12]. For General Hyperbolic Systems see Kreiss [26], Parlett [34].

but this is unstable, as can easily be shown, using exponential solutions. A choice which works is obtained by considering

$$\frac{p(x, t+k) - \dfrac{p(x+h, t) + p(x-h, t)}{2}}{k} = \frac{q(x+h, t) - q(x-h, t)}{2h}$$

and doing the same for q.

In matrix notation with $\lambda = k/h$

$$U(x, t+k) = \begin{pmatrix} \frac{1}{2} & -\frac{\lambda}{2} \\ -\frac{\lambda}{2} & \frac{1}{2} \end{pmatrix} U(x-h, t) + \begin{pmatrix} \frac{1}{2} & \frac{\lambda}{2} \\ \frac{\lambda}{2} & \frac{1}{2} \end{pmatrix} U(x+h, t) .$$

Reverting to the earlier notation V for the solution of the difference equation, we have corresponding to an inhomogeneous system of differential equations

$$U_t = \begin{pmatrix} 0 & \frac{\partial}{\partial x} \\ \frac{\partial}{\partial x} & 0 \end{pmatrix} U + W(x, t)$$

the difference scheme

$$V(x, t+k) = \begin{pmatrix} \frac{1}{2} & -\frac{\lambda}{2} \\ -\frac{\lambda}{2} & \frac{1}{2} \end{pmatrix} V(x-h, t)$$

$$+ \begin{pmatrix} \frac{1}{2} & \frac{\lambda}{2} \\ \frac{\lambda}{2} & \frac{1}{2} \end{pmatrix} V(x+h, t) + kW(x, t)$$

$$= AV(x-h, t) + BV(x+h, t) + kW(x, t) \tag{1.2}$$

where

$$A = \begin{pmatrix} \frac{1}{2} & -\frac{\lambda}{2} \\ -\frac{\lambda}{2} & \frac{1}{2} \end{pmatrix} \quad \text{and} \quad B = \begin{pmatrix} \frac{1}{2} & \frac{\lambda}{2} \\ \frac{\lambda}{2} & \frac{1}{2} \end{pmatrix}.$$

For our initial conditions we have $U(x, 0) = F(x) = V(x, 0)$.

Here A and B are both positive semi-definite symmetric matrices. (i.e. $U^*AU \geqslant 0$ for all U), if the stability condition $\lambda \leqslant 1$ is satisfied.* In addition $A + B = 1$. We will need the following result for a positive semi-definite A and arbitrary vectors X and Y.

$$X^*AY \leqslant \frac{X^*AX + Y^*AY}{2}. \tag{1.2a}$$

[Since A is positive semi-definite

$$0 \leqslant (X - Y)^* A(X - Y) = X^*AX + Y^*AY - X^*AY - Y^*AX.$$

But

$$Y^*AX = (X^*A^*Y^{**})^* = X^*A^*Y^{**} = X^*AY$$

so that

$$0 \leqslant X^*AX + Y^*AY - 2X^*AY].$$

From (1.2) we find

$$V^*(x, t + k)\, V(x, t + k) = V^*(x, t + k)\, AV(x - h, t) + V^*(x, t + k)\, BV(x + h, t) + kV^*(x, t + k)\, W(x, t).$$

By (5.14) we have then that

$$V^*(x, t + k)\, V(x, t + k) \leqslant \tfrac{1}{2} V^*(x, t + k)\, AV(x, t + k) + \tfrac{1}{2} V^*(x - h, t)\, AV(x - h, t) + \tfrac{1}{2} V^*(x, t + k)\, BV(x, t + k) + \tfrac{1}{2} V^*(x + h, t)\, BV(x + h, t) + kV^*(x, t + k)\, W(x, t).$$

---

* The asterisk indicates transposition.

Since

$$A + B = 1$$

$$\tfrac{1}{2} V^*(x, t + k)\, AV(x, t + k) + \tfrac{1}{2} V^*(x, t + k)\, BV(x, t + k)$$
$$= \tfrac{1}{2} V^*(x, t + k)\, V(x, t + h)\,,$$

therefore

$$V^*(x, t + k)\, V(x, t + k) \leqslant V^*(x - h, t)\, AV(x - h, t)$$
$$+ V^*(x + h, t)\, BV(x + h, t) + 2kV^*(x, t + k)\, W(x, t)\,. \tag{1.3}$$

We define a norm by

$$\| V \|_t = \Big(\sum_x V^*(x, t)\, V(x, t)\Big)^{1/2}$$

where the sum is extended over all values x of the lattice. Then by (1.3), [observing that x could be replaced by $x + h$ or $x - h$ as the variable of summation]

$$\| V \|^2_{t+k} \leqslant \sum_x [V^*(x, t)\, AV(x, t) + V^*(x, t)\, BV(x, t)$$
$$+ 2kV^*(x, t + k)\, W(w, t)]$$
$$= \sum_x [V^*(x, t)\, V(x, t) + 2kV^*(x, t + k)\, W(x, t)]. \tag{1.4}$$

At this point we make use of the general Cauchy-Schwarz inequality for our norms. We form the positive semi-definite form in λ and μ:

$$0 \leqslant \sum_x (\lambda V^* + \mu W^*)\, (\lambda V + u W)$$
$$= \lambda^2 \| V \|^2 + 2\lambda\mu \sum_x V^* W + \mu^2 \| W \|^2\,.$$

Since it is semi-definite its discriminant is positive or zero

$$\| V \|^2 \| W \|^2 - \Big(\sum_x V^* W\Big)^2 \geqslant 0\,.$$

Therefore (1.4) yields

$$\| V \|_{t+k}^2 \leqslant \| V \|_t^2 + 2k \| V \|_{t+k} \| W \|_t$$

$$\| V \|_{t+k} \leqslant \sqrt{\| V \|_t^2 + k^2 \| W \|_t^2} + k \| W \|_t .$$

Hence

$$\| V \|_{t+k} \leqslant \| V \|_t + 2k \| W \|_t .$$

We use this inequality to estimate the error in the computation of U in the case $W = 0$.

From the Taylor Expansion we have

$$U(x, t + k) - AU(x - h, t) - BU(x + h, t)$$

$$= U(x, t) + kU_t(x, t) + \frac{k^2}{2} \bar{U}_{tt} - AU(x, t) + hAU_x(x, t)$$

$$- \frac{h^2}{2} A\bar{U}_{xx} - BU(x, t) - hBU_x(x, t) - \frac{h^2}{2} B\bar{U}_{xx} \qquad (1.5)$$

where $\bar{U}_{tt}$ and $\bar{U}_{xx}$ stand for vectors whose components are mean values of the components of U_{tt} and U_{xx}. However,

$$U(x, t) - AU(x, t) - BU(x, t) = (I - A - B)\, U(x, t) = 0.$$

Therefore the left hand side of (1.5) is equal to

$$= k \left[\frac{\partial}{\partial t} + \frac{1}{\lambda} (A - B) \frac{\partial}{\partial x}\right] U + 0(h^2 + k^2);$$

but since

$$\frac{1}{\lambda} (A - B) = \begin{pmatrix} 0 & -1 \\ -1 & 0 \end{pmatrix}$$

the first term is identically zero by (1.1). Thus we have the estimate for the truncation error

$$r(x, t) = U(x, t + k) - AU(x - h) - BU(x + h, t) = 0(h^2 + k^2).$$

We now assume that V satisfies the difference equation

$$V(x, t + k) = AV(x - h, t) + BV(x + h, t) + \epsilon(x, t) .$$

Here $\epsilon(x, t)$ stands for the round off error for which we assume an estimate of the form $\sqrt{\epsilon^*\epsilon} \leqslant \epsilon_0$. Our gross accumulated error

$$E(x, t) = V(x, t) - U(x, t)$$

satisfies the recursion formula

$$\begin{aligned} E(x, t + k) - AE(x - h, t) - BE(x + h, t) &= \epsilon(x, t) - r(x, t) \\ &= kW(x, t). \end{aligned}$$

Here we have $E(x, 0) = 0$ and

$$W_0 = \text{Max}\,(W^*W)^{1/2} \leqslant \frac{\epsilon}{k} + 0(k)\,.$$

We apply now (5.21) to obtain an estimate for the error E at an arbitrary point (x, t). We have

$$(E^*(x, t)\, E(x, t))^{1/2} \leqslant \| E \|_t \leqslant \| E \|_0 + 2k \sum_{V=0}^{j} \| W \|_{Vk}\,.$$

Now $\| E \|_0 = 0$. Moreover, only the values of W in the domain of dependence of (x, t) with respect to the difference equation contribute to $E(x, t)$. Since the number of lattice points in this domain lying on a line $t =$ constant is $\leqslant (2j + 1)$ for $t = jk$ we find

$$\| W \|_\tau \leqslant (2j + 1)^{1/2}\, W_0\,.$$

Consequently we have the final error estimate

$$\begin{aligned} (E^*(x, t)\, E(x, t))^{1/2} &\leqslant 2t(2j + 1)^{1/2}\, W_0 \\ &\leqslant 0\left(\epsilon \left(\frac{t}{k}\right)^{3/2} + t^{3/2}k^{1/2}\right). \end{aligned}$$

This shows that the accumulated truncation error represented by the second term tends to zero as $k \to 0$.

2. The General Symmetric Hyperbolic System

We now consider general symmetric systems of Linear partial differential equations. These systems are not the most general hyperbolic systems; however, they do include nearly all the equations of mathematical physics.

We start with a set of N functions in $n + 1$ independent variables:

$$u_1(t, x_1, \cdots, x_n), \qquad u_2(t, x_1, \cdots, x_n), \qquad \cdots, \qquad u_N(t, x_1, \cdots, x_n).$$

As usual, we work in vector notation

$$U = \begin{pmatrix} u_1 \\ \vdots \\ u_N \end{pmatrix}$$

$$A^l = (a^l_{ij}) \qquad B = (b_{ij}).$$

The general first order linear system can then be written in the form

$$A^0(x, t)\frac{\partial U}{\partial t} + \sum_{l=1}^{n} A^l(x, t)\frac{\partial U}{\partial x_l} + BU = 0 \tag{2.1}$$

where the A^l and B are functions of x and t but not of u.

Hyperbolic are called those equations for which solutions to the Cauchy Problem exist. In particular, for constant coefficients there are exponential solutions, from which all others can be built up by Fourier Transformations. We consider the case where A^0 and A^l are constant matrices and $B = 0$. Then there are solutions of the form

$$U = C \exp i \left(\tau t + \sum_i \xi_i x_i\right)$$

where C is a constant vector. This expression is bounded for all real ξ_i if $t = 0$. We want a condition which assures that τ is real so that U is bounded for all t. We form

$$\frac{\partial U}{\partial x_l} = i\xi_l U$$

$$\frac{\partial U}{\partial t} = i\tau U.$$

If we substitute these back into the original equation (2.1) we find

$$\left(\tau A^0 + \sum \xi_l A^l\right) C = 0. \tag{2.2}$$

When C is not zero we must have

$$\det\left(\tau A^0 + \sum_{l=1}^{n} \xi_l A^l\right) = 0 . \tag{2.3}$$

Thus we are led to the condition that (2.3) should have only real roots τ for any real ξ, if the Cauchy problem is to be well posed. This is essentially the condition which is also used for systems with variable coefficients to define hyperbolicity. More precisely one requires that for every x, t there exist N real linearly independent vectors C annihilated by a matrix $(\tau A^0 + \Sigma_l \xi_l A^j)$.

We shall call the system (2.1) *symmetric hyperbolic* if A^0, $A^1, \cdots, A^n$ are symmetric and A^0 is positive definite. Since we required ξ_i real we can set $\Sigma \xi_l A^l = \Gamma$ and still have Γ symmetric and real. Our problem is to prove $\det(\tau A^0 + \Gamma) = 0$ has only real solutions τ. There is a theorem in linear algebra which states that two quadratic forms, one of which is definite, can be transformed simultaneously to principal axes; that means: if A^0 is symmetric positive definite and Γ is at least symmetric there exists a real, non-singular T such that $T^* A^0 T = \alpha$ and $T^* \Gamma T = \gamma$ where α and γ are real diagonal matrices. Hence the equation $\det(\tau\alpha + \gamma) = 0$ follows from (2.3) which yields that one of the N equations

$$\tau\alpha_i + \gamma_i = 0 \qquad i = 1, \cdots, N \tag{6.14}$$

holds, where α_i and γ_i are the i-th diagonal elements of the matrices α and γ. Since these are real and the α_i are positive, τ must be real. Equation (2.2) becomes $(\tau\alpha + \gamma)\, c = 0$, where $c = T^{-1}C$ is any coordinate vector. This shows that symmetric hyperbolic systems are hyperbolic in the sense defined above.

3. Examples

We will exhibit examples of partial differential equations which can be put into symmetric hyperbolic form. As a first example we have Maxwell's Equations. These are, in vector notation,

$$\nabla \times H = \frac{\epsilon}{C} E_t$$

$$-\nabla \times E = \frac{\mu}{C} H_t .$$

Written out component wise they become

$$\frac{\epsilon}{C} E_{1t} = H_{3y} - H_{2z}$$

$$\cdot \quad \cdot \quad \cdot$$

$$\frac{\mu}{C} H_{3t} = E_{1y} - E_{2x} \,.$$

Then Maxwell's Equation in our notation go over into a system of equations for

$$U = \begin{pmatrix} E_1 \\ E_2 \\ E_3 \\ H_1 \\ H_2 \\ H_3 \end{pmatrix}$$

with matrices

$$A^0 = \left\| \begin{array}{cccccc} \frac{\epsilon}{C} & 0 & 0 & \cdots & & \\ 0 & \frac{\epsilon}{C} & 0 & 0 & & \\ 0 & 0 & \frac{\epsilon}{C} & 0 & & \\ \cdot & 0 & 0 & \frac{\mu}{C} & 0 & \cdot \\ & & 0 & 0 & \frac{\mu}{C} & 0 \\ & & & \cdots & 0 & \frac{\mu}{C} \end{array} \right\|$$

$$A^1 = \left\| \begin{array}{cccccc} 0 & 0 & 0 & \cdots & 0 & 0 \\ 0 & 0 & \cdots & & 0 & 1 \\ \cdots & & & & -1 & 0 \\ \cdots & & & 0 & 0 & 0 \\ \cdots & & & & & \\ 0 & 0 & -1 & & \cdots & \\ 0 & 1 & 0 & & \cdots & \end{array} \right\|$$

and simularly for A^2 and A^3. It is clear that A^0 is symmetric definite and A^1, A^2 and A^3 are symmetric.

Any second order hyperbolic linear equation can also be put in this form. Take, for simplicity, an equation of the form

$$u_{tt} = \sum_{i,k} a_{ik} u_{x_i x_k} + \sum b_i u_{x_i} + c u_t = 0$$

where a_{ik} is definite symmetric. Then, in our form, the equation becomes

$$\begin{pmatrix} 1 & 0 & \cdots & 0 \\ 0 & a_{11} & \cdots & a_{1n} \\ 0 & a_{21} & \cdots & a_{2n} \\ \cdot & \cdot & \cdot & \\ 0 & a_{2n} & \cdots & a_{nn} \end{pmatrix} U_t = \sum_l \begin{pmatrix} 0 & a_{1l} & a_{2l} & \cdots & a_{nl} \\ a_{1l} & 0 & 0 & \cdots & 0 \\ \vdots & & & & \\ a_{nl} & 0 & 0 & \cdots & 0 \end{pmatrix} U_{x_l} + \begin{pmatrix} c & b_1 & \cdots & b_n \\ 0 & 0 & \cdots & \\ \cdot & \cdot & \cdot & \\ 0 & 0 & \cdots & \end{pmatrix} U$$

where U is a vector with components $u_t, u_{x_1}, \cdots, u_{x_n}$.

4. The Difference Scheme. Boundedness of Solutions in the L_2-Sense

We now develop the Friedrichs difference scheme for the solution of symmetric systems. We define in the (x, t) space a lattice with

$$\Delta x_i = h_i$$
$$\Delta_t = k = h_0$$

and the operator E^i with the property that

$$E^i f(x_1, \cdots, x_n, t) = f(x_1, \cdots, x_{i-1}, x_i + h_i, x_{i+1}, \cdots, t)$$
$$E^{-i} f(x_1, \cdots, x_n, t) = f(x_1, \cdots, x_{i-1}, x_i - h_i, x_{i+1}, \cdots, t)$$
$$E^0 f(x_1, \cdots, x_n, t) = f(x_1, \cdots, x_n, t + h_0).$$

We want to form a difference scheme. The natural difference analogue of V_t would be $(E^0V - V)/h_0$. Unfortunately the corresponding difference scheme diverges. We try instead to replace (2.1) by the difference equation

$$A^0 \frac{E^0 - \frac{1}{2n}\sum_{l=1}^{n}(E^l + E^{-l})}{h_0} V(x, t) = \sum_{l=1}^{n} A^l \left(\frac{E^l - E^{-l}}{2h_l}\right) V + BV + W,$$

Introducing $h_0/h_l = \lambda_l$, we have

$$A^0E^0V = \frac{1}{2n}\sum_l A^0(E^l + E^{-l})\,V + \sum_l \tfrac{1}{2}\lambda_l A^l(E^l - E^{-l})\,V + h_0BV + h_0W.$$

Then

$$A^0E^0V = \sum_l \left(\frac{1}{2n}A^0 + \tfrac{1}{2}\lambda_l A^l\right) E^lV + \sum_l \left(\frac{1}{2n}A^0 - \tfrac{1}{2}\lambda_l A^l\right) E^{-l}V + h_0BV + h_0W.$$

Put

$$\alpha^l = \frac{1}{2n}A^0 + \tfrac{1}{2}\lambda_l A^l.$$

$$\alpha^{-l} = \frac{1}{2n}A^0 - \tfrac{1}{2}\lambda_l A^l \tag{4.1}$$

Therefore

$$A^0E^0V = \sum_l \alpha^lE^lV + \sum_l \alpha^{-l}E^{-l}V + h_0BV + h_0W. \tag{4.2}$$

Here α^l and α^{-l} are both symmetric, $\Sigma_l\,(\alpha^l + \alpha^{-l}) = A^0$, and are positive definite if the λ_l are sufficiently small. Taking k so small that the matrices α^l, α^{-l} are positive definite is precisely our *stability condition* here. Keeping in mind our previous result (1.2a)

$$V^*\alpha^lU \leqslant \tfrac{1}{2}(V^*\alpha^lV + U^*\alpha^lU)$$

we find

$$(E^0V)^* A^0(E^0V) = \sum_l (E^0V)^* \alpha^l(E^lV) + \sum_l (E^0V)^* \alpha^{-l}(E^{-l}V)$$

$$+ h_0(E^0V)^* BV + h_0(E^0V)^* W .$$

$$\leqslant \tfrac{1}{2}\sum_l (E^0V)^* \alpha^l(E^0V) + \tfrac{1}{2}\sum_l (E^lV)^* \alpha^l(E^lV)$$

$$+ \tfrac{1}{2}\sum_l (E^0V)^* \alpha^{-l}(E^0V) + \tfrac{1}{2}\sum_l (E^{-l}V)^* \alpha^{-l}(E^{-l}V)$$

$$+ h_0(E^0V)^* BV + h_0(E^0V)^* W .$$

This reduces to

$$(E^0V)^* A^0(E^0V) \leqslant \sum [(E^lV)^* \alpha^l(E^lV + (E^{-l}V)^* \alpha^{-l}(E^{-l}V)]$$

$$+ 2h_0(E^0V)^* (BV + W). \qquad (4.3)$$

We will have to make use of the Cauchy initial conditions $U(x, 0) = F(x)$. We assume $V(x, 0) = F(x)$ where $F = 0$ for large $| x |$.

We have generally

$$E^0[\sigma(x, t)\, \tau(x, t)] = \sigma(x, t + h_0)\, \tau(x, t + h_0) = (E^0\sigma)(E^0\tau) .$$

Then

$$E^0(V^*A^0V) = (E^0V)^* (E^0A^0) (E^0V)$$

$$= (E^0V)^* A^0(E^0V) + (E^0V)^* (E^0A^0 - A^0) (E^0V) .$$

Here, if the coefficients are differentiable $(E^0A^0 - A^0) = 0(h_0)$. Therefore, by (4.3),

$$E^0(V^*A^0V) \leqslant \sum_l [E^l(V^*\alpha^lV) + E^{-l}(V^*\alpha^{-l}V)]$$

$$+ 0\left(h_0 | E^0V |^2 + \sum_l h_l | E^lV |^2 + h_0 | V |^2 + h_0 | W |^2\right) . \qquad (4.4)$$

We sum (4.4) with respect to x. We define the norm $\| V \|_t$ by

$$\| V \|_t^2 = \sum_x V^*(x, t) \, A^0(x, t) \, V(x, t)$$

so that

$$\begin{aligned} \| V \|_{t+h_0}^2 &\leqslant \sum_x \sum_l \overset{*}{V} (\alpha^l + \alpha^{-l}) V + 0 \Big(h_0 \| V \|_{t+h_0}^2 + \sum_l h_l \| V \|_t^2 \\ &\qquad + h_0 \| V \|_t^2 + h_0 \| W \|_t^2 \Big) \\ &= \| V \|_t^2 + 0 \Big(h_0 \| V \|_{t+h_0}^2 + \sum_l h_l \| V \|_t^2 + h_0 \| V \|_t^2 \\ &\qquad + h_0 \| W \|_t^2 \Big) . \end{aligned}$$

Letting μ_{max} and μ_{min} equal the greatest and least eigenvalues of A^0 we know

$$\mu_{\max} V^* V \geqslant V^* A^0 V \geqslant \mu_{\min} V^* V$$

$$| V |^2 = V^* V \leqslant \frac{1}{\mu_{\min}} V^* A^0 V$$

so that

$$\sum_x | V |^2 \leqslant \frac{1}{\mu_{\min}} \sum_x V^* A V = \frac{1}{\mu_{\min}} \| V \|^2 .$$

We will write $v(t)$ for $\| V \|$ and $w(t)$ for $\| W \|_t$. Then

$$v^2(t + h_0) \leqslant v^2(t) + M h_0 [v^2(t + h_0) + v^2(t) + w^2(t)] .$$

with some constant M. Now, since

$$w(t) = \| w \|_t \leqslant \operatorname*{Max}_{0 \leqslant \tau \leqslant t} \| w \|_\tau = \omega(t)$$

we have

$$v^2(t + h_0) \leqslant \frac{1 + M h_0}{1 - M h_0} v^2(t) + \frac{M h_0}{1 - M h_0} \omega^2(t)$$

and

$$v^2(t) \leqslant \left(\frac{1 + Mh_0}{1 - Mh_0}\right)^{t/h_0} v^2(0)$$
$$+ \frac{Mh_0}{1 - Mh_0}\left[1 + \left(\frac{1 + Mh_0}{1 - Mh_0}\right) + \cdots + \left(\frac{1 + Mh_0}{1 - Mh_0}\right)^{(t/h_0)-1}\right]\omega^2 .$$

However,

$$\frac{1 + Mh_0}{1 - Mh_0} = 1 + \frac{2Mh_0}{1 - Mh_0} \leqslant \exp\left(\frac{2Mh_0}{1 - Mh_0}\right).$$

Therefore using that $e^x - 1 < xe^x$ for $x \geqslant 0$

$$V^2(t) \leqslant \exp\left(\frac{2M}{1 - Mh_0}t\right)\left[v^2(0) + \frac{Mt}{1 - Mh_0}\omega^2\right]. \tag{4.5}$$

In all this we have tacitly assumed $1 - Mh_0 > 0$. This condition will be satisfied if h_0 is small enough. Our resulting apriori estimate is finally

$$\| V \|_t \leqslant \exp\left(\frac{M}{1 - Mh_0}t\right)\left(\| F \| + \left(\frac{Mt}{1 - Mh_0}\right)^{1/2} \operatorname*{Max}_{0 \leqslant \tau \leqslant t} \| W \|_\tau\right). \tag{4.6}$$

5. Estimates for the Norms of Difference Quotients

For the purpose of discussing pointwise convergence of the difference scheme we shall also need estimates analogous to (4.6) for the divided difference of the solution V of (4.2). We introduce a difference quotient

$$\frac{E^l V - V}{h_l} = \delta_l V; \qquad l = 0, \cdots, n$$

where $h_0 = k$ is in the t direction and h_l is in the x_l direction. Differencing both sides of the equation (4.2) for V we have

$$(A^0)(E^0\delta_l V) = \sum_j (\alpha^j E^j + \alpha^{-j}E^{-j})\delta_l V$$
$$+ kB\delta_l V + k\delta_l W - (\delta_l A^0)(E^0 E^l V)$$
$$+ \sum_j [(\delta_l \alpha^j)(E^j E^l V) + (\delta_l \alpha^{-j})(E^{-j}E^l V)] + k(\delta_l B)(E^l V). \tag{5.1}$$

[We have used the fact that the difference of a product is

$$\begin{aligned}\delta_l(fg) &= \frac{E^l(fg) - fg}{h_l} = \frac{(E^l f)(E^l g) - fg}{h_l} \\ &= \frac{f(E^l g - g) + (E^l f - f)(E^l g)}{h_l} \\ &= f\delta_l(g) + \delta_l(f)(E^l(g))] .\end{aligned}$$

(5.1) is an inhomogeneous difference equation for $\delta_l V$ of a type similar to (4.2). Direct application of the estimate (4.5) leads to some difficulty since the inhomogeneous part does not contain everywhere a factor of order k. We can, however, modify the equation using the identity

$$\sum_{j=1}^{n} (\alpha^{-j} + \alpha^{j}) = A^0$$

which implies $\delta_l \alpha^j + \delta_l \alpha^{-j} = \delta_l A^0$. We have

$$(\delta_l A^0)(E^0 E^l V) = (\delta_l A^0)(E^l V) + h_0(\delta_l A^0)(E^l \delta_0 V)$$

Then (5.1) becomes

$$\begin{aligned}A^0(E^0\delta_l V) &= \sum_j (\alpha^j E^j + \alpha^{-j}E^{-j})\,\delta_l V + kB\delta_l V + k\delta_l W \\ &\quad - h_0(\delta_l A^0)(E^l\delta_0 V) + \sum_j h_j(\delta_l \alpha^j)(E^l \delta_j V) \\ &\quad - \sum_j h_j(\delta_l \alpha^{-j})(E^{-l}E^{-j})(\delta_j V) + k(\delta_l B)(E^l V) \qquad (5.2)\end{aligned}$$

(here we used $E^{-j} - 1 = - h_j E^{-j}\delta_j$). We can assume that all the h_j are of the same order of magnitude as k. Then the inhomogeneous part in (5.2) is of order k. We find applying (4.5) that for bounded t

$$\| \delta_l V \|_t^2 = 0\left(\| \delta_l V \|_0^2 + t \operatorname*{Max}_{0\leqslant\tau\leqslant t}\left[\| \delta_l W \|_\tau^2 + \sum_{j=0}^{n} \| \delta_j V \|_\tau^2 + \| V \|_\tau^2\right)\right].$$

Hence

$$\operatorname*{Max}_{\substack{l\\0\leqslant\tau\leqslant t}} \| \delta_l V \|_\tau^2 = 0\Big(\operatorname*{Max}_{\substack{l\\0\leqslant\tau\leqslant t}} [\| \delta_l V \|_0^2 + t \| \delta_l V \|_\tau^2 + t \| \delta_l W \|_\tau^2 + t \| W \|_\tau^2 + t \| V \|_0^2]\Big).$$

For t not too large this implies

$$\operatorname*{Max}_{l=0,\dots,n} \| \delta_l V \|_{t=0}^2 = 0\Big(\| F \|^2 + \sum_l \| \delta_l F \|^2 + \| W \|^2 + \operatorname*{Max}_{l,t} \| \delta_l W \|_t\Big). \tag{5.3}$$

Thus we obtain finally an estimate for the norm of the first difference quotients of V in terms of the norms of F, W, and their first difference quotients. We can proceed similarly and obtain estimates for the norm of any difference quotients of V of order k in terms of the norms of difference quotients F and W of orders less than or equal to k.

6. Sobolev's Lemma for Functions on a Lattice

A lemma, due to Sobolev, permits to estimate V itself at one point in terms of the norms of V and its difference quotients of sufficiently high order. We shall prove the lemma first for functions $f(x_1)$ of a single independent variable x_1 which varies over the set I_1 of lattice points and then extend it by induction to more variables. Let $f(x_1)$ be a function with $f(x_1) = 0$ outside some finite interval (that is f has compact support). Let the lattice points be equidistant poits x_i and assume we have an estimate given for $\Sigma_{I_1} f^2$ and $\Sigma_{I_1} (\delta_1 f)^2$. Take f for two lattice points and subtract

$$f(y_1) - f(x_1) = [f(y_1) - f(y_1 - h_1)] + [f(y_1 - h_1) - f(y_1 - 2h_1)] + \cdots + [f(x_1 + h) - f(x_1)],$$

where h_1 is the mesh width of the lattice. Now assume $x_1 + 1 \geqslant y_1 > x_1$. Squaring both sides and using Schwartz's inequality gives

$$(f(y_1) - f(x_1))^2 \leqslant \frac{1}{h_1} h_1^2 \sum_{I_1} (\delta_1 f)^2$$

since $(y_1 - x_1)/h_1 \leqslant 1/h_1$. Solving for $f(x_1)$:

$$|f(x_1)| \leqslant |f(y_1)| + \sqrt{h_1}\sqrt{\sum_{I_1}(\delta_1 f)^2}.$$

Squaring again and using $(a+b)^2 \leqslant 2a^2 + 2b^2$ we have

$$|f(x_1)|^2 \leqslant 2|f(y_1)|^2 + 2h_1 \sum_{I_1}(\delta_1 f)^2 .$$

Let

$$y_1 = x_1 + h_1 \cdots, x_1 + nh_1 \leqslant x_1 + 1 .$$

Then, adding all the inequalities

$$\left(\frac{1}{h_1} - 1\right)|f(x_1)|^2 \leqslant 2\sum_{I_1} f^2 + 2\sum_{I_1}(\delta_1 f)^2 .$$

Thus, for sufficiently small h_1 we have

$$|f(x_1)|^2 \leqslant 3h_1\left[\sum_{I_1} f^2 + \sum_{I_1}(\delta_1 f)^2\right].$$

We then obtain by induction, for x_2 varying over equidistant points a distance h_2 apart

$$\begin{aligned}|f(x_1, x_2)|^2 &\leqslant 3h_1\left(\sum_{y_1} f^2(y_1, x_2) + \sum_{y_1}[\delta_1 f(y_1, x_2]^2\right)\\ &\leqslant 9h_1h_2\left[\sum_{y_1,y_2} f^2(y_1, y_2)\right] + \sum_{y_1,y_2}[\delta_1 f(y_1, y_2)]^2\\ &\quad + \sum_{y_1,y_2}[\delta_2 f(y_1 y_2)]^2 + \sum_{y_1,y_2}[\delta_1\delta_2 f(y_1, y_2)]^2].\end{aligned}$$

More generally, putting $H = h_1, h_2, \cdots, h_n$,

$$\begin{aligned}|f(x_1, \cdots, x_n)|^2 &\leqslant 3^n h_1 \cdots h_n\left[\sum f^2 + \sum(\delta_1 f)^2 + \cdots\right.\\ &\qquad\left. + \sum(\delta_n f)^2 + \cdots + \sum(\delta_1\delta_2\cdots\delta_n f)^2\right]\\ &= 0(\|f\|^2 + \|\delta_1 f\|^2 + \cdots + \|\delta_n f\|^2\\ &\qquad + \cdots + \|\delta_1\delta_2\cdots\delta_n f\|^2)H. \qquad (6.1)\end{aligned}$$

7. Proof of Convergence for the Difference Scheme

Combining inequality (6.1) with the previously obtained inequalities for V and its difference quotients we find that for t sufficiently small

$$
\begin{aligned}
| V(x_1, \cdots, x_k, t) |^2 &= | V(x, t) |^2 \\
&= 0\left(H\left[\| V \|_t^2 + \| \delta_1 V \|_t^2 + \cdots \| \delta_1 \cdots \delta_2 V \|_t^2\right]\right) \\
&= 0\left(H\left[\| F \|^2 + \| \delta_1 F \|^2 + \cdots + \operatorname*{Max}_{0 \leqslant \tau \leqslant t} \| W \|_\tau^2 + \cdots\right]\right).
\end{aligned}
$$

Let for a fixed point (x^0, t^0) the function $\varphi = \varphi(x)$ be defined so as to have the value 1 for x in the domain of dependence D of (x^0, t^0), and the value 0 for x at a distance > 1 from D. Let moreover φ have bounded derivatives of orders $\leqslant n$. The value $V(x^0, t^0)$ is not affected, if we replace F and W by φF and φW respectively. Moreover

$$
\| \delta_1(\varphi F) \|^2 = 0\left(\sum [| F |^2 + | \delta_1 F |^2]\right),
$$

where the summation is extended over a bounded region only. Hence

$$
\| \delta_1 \varphi F \|^2 = 0\left(\frac{1}{H} \operatorname{Max} (| F |^2 + | \delta_1 F |^2)\right).
$$

Similar estimates hold for the norms of the other difference quotients of φF and φW. It follows then that for t sufficiently small

$$
V(x^0, t^0)^2 = 0(F_n^2 + W_n^2) \tag{7.1}
$$

where F_n is an upper bound for the absolute values of the initial function F and its difference quotients of order $\leqslant n$ and W_n is an upper bound for the absolute values of W and its difference quotients of order $\leqslant n$ for all smaller t values.

We are now in a position to estimate the accumulated truncation error. The individual truncation error is given by

$$
r = A^0 E^0 U - \sum_j (\alpha^j E^j + \alpha^{-j} E^{-j})\, U - kBU - kW .
$$

Expanding by Taylor's Theorem we find, using (2.1), (4.1)

$$
\begin{aligned}
r = {} & A^0U + h_0A^0U_t + \frac{h_0^2}{2}A^0U_{tt} + \cdots \\
& - \sum_j \left(\alpha^j U + \alpha^j h_j U_{x_j} + \alpha^j \frac{h_j^2}{2} U_{x_j x_j} + \cdots\right) \\
& - \sum_j (\alpha^{-j}U - \alpha^{-j}h_j U_{x_j} + \cdots) - kBU - kW \\
= {} & \frac{h_0^2}{2} A_0 U_{tt} + \frac{h_0^3}{6} A^0 U_{tttt} + \cdots - \sum_j \alpha^j \frac{h_j^2}{2} U_{x_j x_j} - \cdots .
\end{aligned}
$$

Thus r at any point is of order k^2, similarly its first difference quotients are of order k^2, etc., if the solution U is sufficiently regular.

We now consider the function $\eta = V - U$. Then η is a solution of the difference equation

$$
A^0E^0\eta = \sum_j (\alpha^j E^j + \alpha^{-j}E^{-j})\,\eta + kB\eta - kk^{-1}r
$$

with initial values $\eta = 0$. The inhomogeneous term in the difference equation for η is $\eta = -r/k$. We can apply inequality (7.1) with $F_n = 0$.

It follows from (7.1) that $|\eta|^2 = 0(k^2)$. Consequently the accumulated truncation error has finally been proved to be of order k at each point. Analogous estimates can be made for the accumulated round off error.

CHAPTER 9

Solution of Hyperbolic Systems of Equations in Two Independent Variables: Method of Courant-Isaacson-Rees*

We consider a system of N unknown functions $u_1(x, y)$, $u_2(x, y)$, $\cdots$, $u_N(x, y)$ which we will write as the vector

$$U(x, y) = \begin{pmatrix} u_1(x, y) \\ u_2(x, y) \\ \vdots \\ u_N(x, y) \end{pmatrix}. \qquad \text{(S)}$$

The general quasi-linear system of first order differential equations has the form

$$AU_x + BU_y = C$$

where the coefficients $A = (a_{ik}(x, y, u_i))$ and $B = (b_{ik}(x, y, u_i))$ are matrices and $C = c_i(x, y, u_i)$ is a vector.

Writing (S) out componentwise gives

$$\sum_k \left(a_{ik}\frac{\partial u_k}{\partial x} + b_{ik}\frac{\partial u_k}{\partial y}\right) = c_i \qquad (i = 1, 2, \cdots, N).$$

We shall bring this equation into characteristic form using a method due to Courant and Lax.† We assume for simplicity that $| B | = \det B \neq 0$. Then we form AB^{-1} and diagonalize it. This can be done if AB^{-1} has real and distinct eigenvalues. This will

* See Courant-Isaacson-Rees [5].

† See Courant-Lax [7].

be taken as the condition for the system to be *hyperbolic*. Therefore we can find a real matrix T such that $TAB^{-1}T^{-1}$ is a diagonal matrix, that is, a matrix

$$\Lambda = \begin{pmatrix} \lambda_1 & & 0 \\ & \ddots & \\ 0 & & \lambda_N \end{pmatrix}$$

where $\lambda_i = \lambda_i(x, y, u_j)$ are real and distinct eigenvalues of AB^{-1}: Now T has real elements and $TA = \Lambda TB = \Lambda b$ if $TB = b$. We have upon multiplying our original equation from the left by T.

$$\Lambda b U_x + b U_y = TC = \bar{C}$$

where b, Λ , and $\bar{C}$ are known functions of x, y and u. The ith equation of this system is

$$\sum_l b_{il} \left(\lambda_i \frac{\partial u_l}{\partial x} + \frac{\partial u_l}{\partial y} \right) = \bar{c}_i \, .$$

We may interpret $\lambda_i \partial u_l / \partial x + \partial u_l / \partial y$ as a directional derivative of u_l. Then the ith equation has all derivatives taken in a fixed direction for all l. (We note that this property is not possessed by the original system of equations.) The characteristic direction of differentiation occuring in the ith equation is given by the condition

$$\frac{dx}{dy} = \lambda_i \, .$$

We shall now introduce a system of difference equations assuming that the system is strictly linear. The more general quasi-linear case can be treated in the same manner. The general linear system in characteristic form can be written

$$\sum_l b_{il} \left(\lambda_i \frac{\partial u_l}{\partial x} + \frac{\partial u_l}{\partial y} \right) = \sum_l c_{il} u_l + d_i \tag{1}$$

where the b_i , λ_i , c_{il} , d_i are known functions of (x, y). At each point $P = (x, y)$ we have the ith characteristic direction defined by

$$\frac{dx}{dy} = \lambda_i(x, y) = \lambda_i(P) \, .$$

Putting

$$\lambda_i \frac{\partial u_l}{\partial x} + \frac{\partial u_l}{\partial y} = \frac{du_l}{dy}$$

we have as our ith equation

$$\sum_l b_{il} \frac{du_l}{dy} = \sum_l c_{il} u_l + d_i . \tag{2}$$

Let us consider the case where the values are to be computed on a discrete set S of points in the x, y plane where these points are grouped arbitrarily on curves $I_0, I_1, \cdots$. We assume that one of these curves, say I_0, carries the initial data for the problem. We shall suppose that we have, starting with the values of U at the points of S on I_0, computed U approximately successively on $I_1, \cdots, I_m$. Let these approximations be denoted by v. Let P be a point on I_{m+1} and select some Q on I_m which is "not far" from P. We want to replace the differential equation by a difference equation. To choose a direction of differentiation we utilize the characteristic directions through Q and take these directions as also giving the correct characteristic directions in P. (This is only important in the non-linear case where the characteristic directions at P are not known precisely without a knowledge of $U(P)$.) The scheme would be simple if each chosen characteristic through P met I_m in a point of S. In general this is not the case. We shall get around this by considering any two points Q_i' and Q_i'' of S on I_m such that if a segment be constructed with them as end points then the ith characteristic from P intersects this segment in a point Q_i^*. Now, determine Q_i^* by linear interpolation from Q_i' to Q_i''. That is

$$Q_i^* = \theta_i Q_i' + (1 - \theta_i) Q_i'' \qquad 0 \leqslant \theta_i \leqslant 1 \qquad (i = 1, 2, \cdots N)$$

where $\theta = \theta_i$ is to be found from

$$\frac{x(P) - x(Q_i^*)}{y(P) - y(Q_i^*)} = \frac{x(P) - \theta x(Q_i') - (1 - \theta)\, x(Q_i'')}{y(P) - \theta y(Q_i') - (1 - \theta)\, y(Q_i'')} = \lambda_i(Q).$$

Correspondingly take

$$V(Q_i^*) = \theta_i V(Q_i') + (1 - \theta_i)\, V(Q_i'')$$

and replace (1) by the difference equation

$$L_i(v) = \sum_l b_{il}(Q) \cdot \frac{v_l(P) - [\theta_i v_l(Q_i') + (1 - \theta_i)\, v_l(Q_i'')]}{y(P) - y(Q_i^*)}$$
$$= \sum_l c_{il}(Q)\, v_l(Q) + d_i(Q). \qquad (3)$$

We shall show that as P, Q, Q_i', Q_i'' and therefore Q_i^* come closer together, v converges to the solution, That is

$$\operatorname{Lim} v_l(P) = u_l(P)$$

as the maximum distance between P, Q, Q_i', Q_i'' becomes small. The stability condition for the scheme is that Q_i' and Q_i'' are separated by the ith characteristic through P. We first solve for $v_l(P)$:

$$\sum_l b_{il}(Q)\, v_l(P) = \theta_i \sum_l b_{il}(Q)\, v_l(Q_i') + (1 - \theta_i) \sum_l b_{il}(Q)\, v_l(Q_i'')$$
$$+ (y(P) - y(Q_i^*)) \left(\sum_l c_{il}(Q)\, v(Q) + d_i(Q) \right).$$

Now $|\, b \,| \neq 0$ and therefore we can solve this system. We define

$$\sum_l b_{il}(P)\, v_l(P) = \bar{v}_i(P).$$

This gives, with the above equation:

$$\bar{v}_i(P) = \theta_i \bar{v}(Q_i') + (1 - \theta_i)\, \bar{v}_i(Q_i'')$$
$$+ [y(P) - y(Q_i^*)]\, L_i(V). \qquad (4)$$

We are essentially interested in the error between U and V if the maximum distance between $P, Q, Q', Q'' = 0(h) \to 0$, where h is the distance between neighboring curves I_m and I_{m+1}. It can easily be seen that

$$L_i(u) = \sum_l c_{il}(Q)\, u_i(Q) + d_i(Q) + 0(h). \qquad (5)$$

Indeed

$$\frac{u_l(P) - u_l(Q_i^*)}{y(P) - y(Q_i^*)} = \left(\frac{du}{dy}\right)_Q + 0(h).$$

The error in determining $u_l(Q_i^*)$ by linear interpolation is $0(h^2)$. Thus

$$\frac{u_l(P) - [\theta_i u_l(Q_i') + (1 - \theta_i)\, u_l(Q_i'')]}{y(P) - y(Q_i^*)} = \left(\frac{du}{dy}\right)_Q + 0(h)\,.$$

We find from (2)

$$L_i(u) = \sum_l b_{il}(Q)\left(\frac{dU_l}{dy}\right)_Q + 0(h)$$

$$= \sum_l c_{il}(Q)\, u_l(Q) + d_i(Q) + 0(h)\,.$$

Let

$$E(P) = v(P) - u(P)\,.$$

This gives by (3), (5)

$$L_i(v) - L_i(u) = L_i(E) = 0(E(Q) + h)\,.$$

Let

$$\bar{E}_i(P) = \sum_l b_{il}(P)\, E_l(P)\,.$$

Now let the *magnitude* $|\, E \,|$ of E at one point be the maximum of the absolute value of any component of $\bar{E}$ and let the norm $\|\, E \,\|_m$ of the error on the mth curve I_m be defined by

$$\|\, E \,\|_m = \operatorname*{Max}_{\substack{\text{all } i \\ \text{all } Q \text{ on } I_m}} |\, E(Q) \,|.$$

We have by (4)

$$\bar{E}_i(P) = \theta_i \bar{E}_i(Q_i') + (1 - \theta_i)\,(\bar{E}_i(Q_i'')) + 0(h\,\|\, E \,\|_m + h^2).$$

Then, since $0 \leqslant \theta_i \leqslant 1$,

$$\|\, E \,\|_{m+1} \leqslant \|\, E \,\|_m + 0(h\,\|\, E \,\|_m + h^2)$$

$$\leqslant \|\, E \,\|_m + Mh(\|\, E \,\|_m + h)$$

$$= (1 + Mh)\,\|\, E \,\|_m + Mh^2.$$

Iterate. Then, for small h we have, letting $\| E \|_0 = 0$:

$$\| E \|_m \leqslant Mh^2[1 + (1 + Mh) + \cdots + (1 + Mh)^{m-1}]$$
$$\leqslant mMh^2(1 + Mh)^{m-1}.$$

Roughly speaking, $mh = Y$ is an upper bound for the distance away from I_0. Assume Y is bounded, then

$$\| E \|_m \leqslant hMYe^{Mh(m+1)} = 0(h).$$

This proves convergence of the scheme.

To carry out the non-linear case take the same type of net and the same form of recursion formula as above. However, now the characteristic directions are not known beforehand. Thus we must use the difference equation

$$\sum_l b_{il}(Q, v(Q)) \frac{v_l(P) - [\theta_i v_l(Q_i') + (1 - \theta_i) v_l(Q_i'')]}{y(P) - y(Q_i^*)} = \bar{C}_i(Q_i, v(Q_i)).$$

Here Q_i^* is found again by linear interpolation with a value of θ determined by the characteristic equation

$$\frac{x(P) - x(Q_i^*)}{y(P) - y(Q_i^*)} = \lambda_i(Q, v(Q)).$$

The characteristic directions for u can be shown to differ from those of v by an error of order h.

CHAPTER 10

An Elliptic Equation: The Equation of Laplace*

1. The Difference Scheme

We consider the equation

$$\Delta u = u_{xx} + u_{yy} = 0 \tag{1.1}$$

in a region R with the condition $u = f$ on the boundary R_b of R. This constitutes the Dirichlet problem for (1.1). We assume a square grid of side h to be imposed upon R. Then our difference operator analogue to Δu is

$$L[v] = \frac{v(x+h, y) - 2v(x, y) + v(x-h, y)}{h^2} + \frac{v(x, y+h) - 2v(x, y) + v(x, y-h)}{h^2}. \tag{1.2}$$

We would like $L[v] = 0$ but have to consider also $L[v] = w$. We shall in the sequel use the following notation: If $(x, y) = P$ is a grid point, then the four points $(x, y-h)$, $(x-h, y)$, $(x, y+h)$, $(x+h, y)$ are *neighbors* of P. We write $Q \sim P$ if Q is a neighbor of P. Solving for $v(P)$ we have

$$v(P) = \tfrac{1}{4} \sum_{Q\sim P} v(Q) - \frac{h^2}{4} L[v(P)]. \tag{1.3}$$

Let r denote the set of lattice points lying in the closed set R. A lattice point P will be called an *interior* lattice point if P and all

* See Young [42], Forsythe and Wasow [41].

its neighbors are in r; the set of interior lattice points will be denoted by r_i. The set r_b of boundary lattice points is defined as the set $r - r_i$. In general the points of r_b do not lie on R_b.

For v defined in r the expression $L(v)$ is defined in r_i. We first consider the following analogue to the Dirichlet problem: Find a function $v(P)$ in r such that $L[v(P)] = w(P)$ is given for $P \in r_i$ and $v(P)$ is given for $P \in r_b$.

2. Existence and Uniqueness of Solutions of the Difference Equation

We first wish to show the existence and uniqueness of a solution. Now we see that the number of unknowns equals the number of P in r which in turn equals the number of conditions given.

We shall derive a maximum principle. Now for $P \in r_i$

$$v(P) = \tfrac{1}{4} \sum_{Q \sim P} v(Q) - \frac{h^2}{4} w(P) . \tag{2.1}$$

We first consider the case where $w(P) > 0$ for $P \in r_i$. Then any solution of (1.3) cannot assume its maximum value in r_i. For if v attains its maximum M at a point $P_0 \in r_i$ we would have

$$\begin{aligned} M &= \operatorname*{Max}_{P \in r} v(P) = v(P_0) \\ &= \tfrac{1}{4} \sum_{Q \sim P_0} v(Q) - \frac{h^2}{4} w(P_0) \leqslant \tfrac{1}{4} \sum_{Q \sim P_0} M - \frac{h^2}{4} w(P_0) < M. \end{aligned}$$

Let w now be arbitrary. Assume $L[v(P)] = w(P)$ for $P \in r_i$. Let

$$M = \operatorname*{Max}_{P \in r} v(P) = v(P_0) .$$

We first assume $P_0 \in r_i$. Form an auxilliary function with positive L. Take

$$\bar{v}(P) = v(P) + \epsilon(\overline{PP_0}^2)$$

where ϵ is constant. Now

$$L[\bar{v}(P)] = L[v(P)] + 4\epsilon = w(P) + 4\epsilon .$$

Choose ϵ large enough such that $L[\bar{v}] > 0$ for all $P \in r_i$. That is

$$\epsilon > \operatorname*{Max}_{P \in r_i} (-\tfrac{1}{4} w(P)) .$$

Then $L[\bar{v}] > 0$ and $\bar{v}$ assumes its maximum on r_b, that is

$$v(P_0) = \bar{v}(P_0) = M < \operatorname*{Max}_{P \in r_b} \bar{v} = \operatorname*{Max}_{P \in r_b} (v(P) + \epsilon(\overline{P_0P^2}))$$
$$\leqslant \operatorname*{Max}_{P \in r_b} v(P) + \epsilon d^2$$

where $d =$ diameter of R. This holds for

$$\epsilon > \operatorname*{Max}_{P \in r_i} (-\tfrac{1}{4} w(P))$$

and hence also for

$$\epsilon = \operatorname*{Max}_{P \in r_i} (-\tfrac{1}{4} w(P)) .$$

Therefore

$$M = v(P_0) \leqslant \operatorname*{Max}_{P \in r_b} v(P) + \frac{d^2}{4} \operatorname*{Max}_{P \in r_i} (-w(P))$$
$$\leqslant \operatorname*{Max}_{P \in r_b} | v(P) | + \frac{d^2}{4} \operatorname*{Max}_{P \in r_i} | w(P) | .$$

Evidently this also holds for P_0 on r_b. Since this applies for $-v$ we obtain

$$| v(P) | \leqslant \operatorname*{Max}_{P \in r_b} | v(P) | + \frac{d^2}{4} \operatorname*{Max}_{P \in r_i} | w(P) | . \tag{2.2}$$

We now show uniqueness by noting that if v vanishes on r_b and $L[v] = 0$ on r_i, then $v \equiv 0$ from (2.2). Thus the homogeneous case has only the trivial solution. Therefore, due to the well known theorem from linear algebra, the inhomogeneous case possesses a unique solution.

It remains to relate the boundary values for the difference equation to those for the differential equation and to obtain an error estimate.

We shall discuss two ways of associating boundary values for v with the boundary values f of u.

(I) If $P_0 \in r_b$ then at least one of its four neighbors is not in r. Then some point $Q \in R_b$ is close to $P_0 : \overline{QP_0} \leqslant h$. We can assign to $v(P_0)$ the value $f(Q)$.

(II) Assume P_0 has two opposite neighbors P_1 and P_3 such that $P_1 \in r_i$ and $P_3 \notin r$. Then there is a point Q of R_b on P_0P_3. We require that

$$v(P_0) = \frac{\theta v(P_1) + f(Q)}{1 + \theta}$$

where $\overline{P_0Q} = \theta h$; $0 \leqslant \theta \leqslant 1$. The assumption on the neighbors of any point of r_b is satisfied; if h is small enough and the boundary is not too irregular. This last equation is another linear equation in our system with f known.

3. Error Estimates

We now derive an error estimate for the first method. Let $\Delta u = 0$ and $u = f$ on R_b and $L[v] = -4\epsilon(P)/h^2$ in r_i. That is

$$v(P) = \tfrac{1}{4} \sum_{L=1}^{4} v(P_i) + \epsilon(P)$$

where $\epsilon(P)$ represents the error in solving the difference scheme. We have also $v(P) = f(Q)$ for $P \in r_b$ where $\overline{PQ} < h$. Set: $E(P) = v(P) - u(P)$. Then $L(E) = L[v] - L[u]$. Here, indicating by a bar suitable intermediate values

$$L[u] = \Delta u + \frac{h^2}{12} \bar{u}_{xxxx} + \frac{h^2}{12} \bar{u}_{yyyy} .$$

Let

$$\operatorname*{Max}_R | u^{IV} | = u_4$$

where u^{IV} refers to all types of fourth derivatives of u. Then $| L[u] | \leqslant h^2 u_4/6$. Assume $| \epsilon(P) | \leqslant \epsilon_0$. Then

$$| L(E) | \leqslant \frac{4}{h^2} \epsilon_0 + \frac{h^2}{6} u_4 \qquad \text{for} \qquad P \in r_i .$$

We still need the error on the boundary. Let $P_0 \in r_b$, then $v(P_0) = f(Q)$ and $u(P_0) = f(Q) \pm hu_1$ where $u_1 = \text{Max} | u^I |$. Therefore

$$| E(P_0) | = | u(P_0) - v(P_0) | \leqslant hu_1 .$$

Now using the maximum principle (2.2)

$$|E(P)| \leqslant hu_1 + \frac{d^2}{h^2}\epsilon_0 + d^2h^2\frac{u_4}{24}.$$

If $\epsilon_0 = 0$ then as $h \to 0$ v converges to the solution u. The accumulated truncation error bound $hu_1 + d^2h^2u_4/24$ is of order h, due to the crude approximation for $v(P)$ on r_b.

To obtain a better result we use method II. We have the system of equations:

$$\text{(a)} \qquad L[v] = -\frac{4}{h^2}\epsilon(P) \qquad \text{for} \qquad P \in r_i$$

$$\text{(b)} \qquad (1+\theta)v(P_0) - \theta v(P_1) = f(Q) + \frac{\epsilon(P_0)}{h^2}, \quad P_0 \in r_b \text{ and } P_1 \in r_i.$$

(We permit an error ϵ/h^2 in the boundary condition.) Let

$$\epsilon_0 = \operatorname*{Max}_{r} |\epsilon(P)|.$$

There are now as many equations as there are unknowns. If v exists we would get the following estimate

$$\operatorname*{Max}_{r} |v(P)| \leqslant \operatorname*{Max}_{r_b} |v| + \frac{d^2}{4}\operatorname*{Max}_{r_i} |L[v]|$$

$$\leqslant \operatorname*{Max}_{r_b} |v| + \frac{d^2}{h^2}\epsilon_0.$$

Now for P_0 in r_b

$$|v(P_0)| = \left| \frac{\theta v(P_1) + f(Q) + \epsilon(P_0)\left(\frac{1}{h^2}\right)}{1+\theta} \right|$$

$$\leqslant \tfrac{1}{2}\operatorname*{Max}_{r} |v| + \operatorname*{Max}_{R_b} |f(Q)| + \frac{\epsilon_0}{h^2}.$$

Hence

$$\operatorname*{Max}_{r} |v(P)| \leqslant \tfrac{1}{2}\operatorname*{Max}_{r} |v| + \operatorname*{Max}_{R_b} |f(Q)| + \frac{\epsilon_0}{h^2} + \frac{d^2}{h^2}\epsilon_0$$

or

$$\operatorname*{Max}_{r} |v(P)| \leqslant 2\operatorname*{Max}_{R_b} |f(Q)| + 2\frac{\epsilon_0}{h^2}(1+d^2).$$

For $\epsilon_0 = 0$, $f = 0$ we can conclude that $v = 0$. This uniqueness theorem for v again implies existence of a solution.

Applying the same argument to $E = v - u$ we have

$$\operatorname*{Max}_{P \in r} | E(P) | \leqslant \operatorname*{Max}_{r_b} | E | + \frac{d^2}{4} \operatorname*{Max}_{r_i} | L(E) |$$

$$\leqslant \operatorname*{Max}_{r_b} | E | + \frac{\epsilon_0 d^2}{h^2} + \frac{d^2 h^2}{24} u_4 .$$

If $P_0 \in r_b$ we have, since linear interpolation is correct to terms of the second order,

$$u(P_0) = \frac{f(Q) + \theta u(P_1)}{1 + \theta} + 0(h^2 u_2) .$$

Therefore

$$E(P_0) = \frac{\theta}{1 + \theta} E(P_1) \pm \frac{\epsilon_0}{h^2(1 + \theta)} \pm 0(h^2 u_2)$$

and

$$\operatorname*{Max}_{r_t} | E | \leqslant \tfrac{1}{2} \operatorname*{Max}_{r} | E | + \frac{\epsilon_0}{h^2} + 0(h^2 u_2)$$

$$\operatorname*{Max}_{r} | E | \leqslant \tfrac{1}{2} \operatorname*{Max}_{r} | E | + \frac{\epsilon_0}{h^2} + 0(h^2 u_2) + \frac{\epsilon_0 d^2}{h^2} + \frac{d^2 h^2}{24} u_4 .$$

Therefore

$$\operatorname*{Max}_{r} | E | \leqslant \frac{2\epsilon_0}{h^2} (1 + d^2) + 0(h^2(u_2 + u_4)) .$$

In this case the accumulated truncation error is of the order h^2. One might be tempted to improve accuracy by using approximations v corresponding to two different mesh sizes h as was discussed before in other examples. (see p. 105). It has been shown, however,* that the accumulated truncation error while of order h^2 has an oscillating coefficient. Hence the method II of taking into account the boundary data is not sufficiently refined to permit extrapolation with respect to h.

In the estimates for the truncation error the bounds u_1, u_2, u_4

* See Wasow [41].

for the derivatives of u enter. The question remains how to estimate these quantities from a knowledge of the boundary values f alone. One method to get such estimates consists in mapping the region R, if it is simply connected, into a circle. u goes over into a harmonic function $\bar{u}$ in the unit circle. Bounds for kth derivatives of u can be obtained in terms of bounds for derivatives of $\bar{u}$ of order $\leqslant k$ and of derivatives of the mapping function. If the boundary of R is sufficiently smooth the mapping function will have bounded derivatives. Hence we only have to estimate derivatives of a harmonic function $\bar{u}$ in the unit circle.

We have in polar coordinates

$$\bar{u} = \sum_{n=0}^{\infty} (a_n \cos n\theta + b_n \sin n\theta)\, r^n$$

and for the boundary values

$$f = \sum_{n=0}^{\infty} (a_n \cos n\theta - b_n \sin n\theta)\,.$$

Then

$$\bar{u}_4 = 0\left(\sum_{n=0}^{\infty} (|\, a_n \,| + |\, b_n \,|)\, n^4\right).$$

Here, if f has continuous sixth derivatives,

$$\begin{aligned} b_n &= \frac{1}{\pi}\int_{-\pi}^{\pi} f \sin n\theta \, d\theta \\ &= -\frac{1}{\pi n^6}\int_{-\pi}^{\pi} f^{VI} \sin n\theta \, d\theta \\ &= 0\left(\frac{1}{n^6} F_6\right) \end{aligned}$$

where F_6 is max $|\, f^{VI} \,|$. Similarly for a_n. Hence

$$\bar{u}_4 = 0\left(F_6 \sum_{1}^{\infty} \frac{1}{n^2}\right).$$

It follows that the derivatives of u of order $\leqslant 4$ can be estimated in terms of derivatives of F of order $\leqslant 6$.

We can then prove that our difference schemes converge even if f is only assumed to be continuous. For this purpose we approximate f uniformly by a sequence of functions $f_n \in C^6$. For $n \to \infty$ the corresponding solutions u_n will converge towards a solution u with boundary values f by the maximum principle. Similarly the solutions v_n of the difference equation for fixed h will converge towards v. There exists an N such that $| u_N - u | < \epsilon$, $| v_N - v | < \epsilon$. Also if h is sufficiently small $| v_N - u_N | < \epsilon$. Hence, $| u - v | < 3\epsilon$ for h sufficiently small.

4. Numerical Solution of the Difference Scheme

We next discuss the numerical solution of the difference equation by iteration. We consider the situation for Method I. We had

$$v(P) = \tfrac{1}{4} \sum_{Q \sim P} v(Q) \qquad \text{for} \qquad P \in r_i \tag{4.1}$$

$$v(P) = f(P) \qquad \text{for} \qquad P \in r_b \,. \tag{4.2}$$

where $f(P)$ is taken as the value of f in some neighboring point of R_b. We define for any two lattice points P and Q

$$C^R_{PQ} = \begin{cases} \tfrac{1}{4} & \text{if} \quad P, Q \in r_i\,, P \sim Q \\ 0 & \text{otherwise} \end{cases}$$

$$d^R_{PQ} = \begin{cases} \tfrac{1}{4} & \text{if} \quad P \in r_i\,, Q \in r_b\,, P \sim Q \\ 0 & \text{otherwise}\,. \end{cases}$$

The two above equations (4.1), (4.2) for v reduce them to

$$v(P) = \sum_Q C^R_{PQ}\, v(Q) + \sum_Q d^R_{PQ} f(Q)$$

for a point $P \in r_i$. For $P \notin r_i$ this formula gives $v(P) = 0$.

We want to solve these equations by iteration. That is, we define a sequence of functions using the recursion formulae:

$$v^{n+1}(P) = \sum_Q C^R_{PQ}\, v^n(Q) + \sum_Q d^R_{PQ} f(Q)\,.$$

We shall show that this method converges. The question is how rapidly? Write the formula as a linear transformation

$$v^{n+1} = C^R v^n + D^R f \tag{4.3}$$

where C^R and D^R are the appropriate matrices. These matrices are infinite but contain only a finite number of non-zero elements, corresponding to the lattice points that lie in R, so that the theory for finite matrices applies. Convergence depends upon $(C^R)^n \to 0$ with $n \to \infty$. That is, we must require the eigenvalues of λ of C^R to satisfy $|\lambda| < 1$. This is easily seen to be satisfied from the maximum principle.

We shall, however, obtain a finer estimate.

The matrix C^R is symmetric; hence all its eigenvalues λ_i are real. Let

$$\lambda_R = \operatorname*{Max}_i \lambda_i .$$

Then the eigenvalue λ_R and the corresponding eigenvector w can be characterized by the fact that the expression

$$\frac{\sum_{P,Q} C^R_{PQ}\, v(P)\, v(Q)}{\sum_P v(P)\, v(P)} \tag{4.4}$$

has the maximum λ_R and reaches it for $v = w$. It is clear that the expression (4.4) increases when v is replaced by its absolute value, unless v has the same sign in any two neighboring points. Assume that r_i is *connected* in the sense that each point of r_i can be joined to any other point by a chain of neighboring points. Then necessarily $w(P) > 0$ for all P in r_i. Hence there exists a positive eigenfunction to the eigenvalue λ_R.

Let now v be any eigenfunction belonging to an eigenvalue λ, so that $C^R v = \lambda v$. Let

$$\mu = \operatorname*{Max}_{P \in r_i} \left| \frac{v(P)}{w(P)} \right| .$$

Then

$$|\lambda|\,|v(P)| = |\lambda v(P)| = \left| \sum_Q C^R_{PQ}\, v(Q) \right|$$

$$\leqslant \sum_Q C^R_{PQ}\, \mu w(Q) = \mu \lambda_R w(P).$$

Hence also $| v(P)| / w(P) \leqslant \mu\lambda_R / | \lambda |$ for all P in r_i, and thus $| \lambda | \leqslant \lambda_R$. Hence

$$\lambda_R = \operatorname*{Max}_i | \lambda_i |.$$

From

$$\lambda_R w(P) = \sum_Q C^R_{PQ} \, w(Q)$$

we obtain by addition over all P

$$\lambda_R \sum_P w(P) = \sum_Q w(Q) \sum_P C^R_{PQ} < \sum_Q w(Q)$$

so that $\lambda_R < 1$. We have then for the recursive functions v^n of (4.3)

$$v^{n+1} - v^n = 0(\lambda_R{}^n),$$

giving convergence in terms of a geometric series. A difficulty arises because λ_R is close to 1 and becomes closer as the mesh is refined. We shall now develop an upper and a lower estimate for λ_R. We do this utilizing the fact that λ_R can be computed exactly for a proper type of rectangle and by noting that λ_R depends in a monotonically increasing manner upon the region R.

We consider two regions $R \subset R'$. Assume that $\lambda_{R'}$ is the largest eigenvalue of the matrix $C^{R'}$; then there exists a non-negative corresponding eigenfunction w of $C^{R'}$.

Now $R \subset R'$ implies $0 \leqslant C^R_{PQ} \leqslant C^{R'}_{PQ}$. It follows from the representation of λ_R as extremum of the expression (4.4) for non-negative v that $\lambda_R \leqslant \lambda_{R'}$.

Similarly we obtain a lower bound $\lambda_{R'} \leqslant \lambda_R$ in case $R' \subset R$.

It remains to find suitable regions R' for which the maximum eigenvalue $\lambda_{R'}$ can be determined.

Take for R' a rectangle with sides of length $a = nh$ and $b = mh$ where the grid is of mesh h and two adjacent sides of the rectangle coincide with the coordinate axis. We can, in this case, write down the solution of the difference equation explicitly since $r_b{}'$ coincides with the mesh points on the boundary of R'. Take

$$w(P) = w(x, y) = \sin \frac{\pi x}{nh} \sin \frac{\pi y}{mh} \qquad \text{for} \qquad P \in r_i{}'$$

and $w(P) = 0$ for P not in r_i'. It is easy to see that w is an eigenfunction for $C^{R'}$

$$\sum_Q C^R_{PQ}\, w(Q) = \mu' w(P) \qquad \text{with} \qquad \mu' = \cos\frac{\pi}{n}\cos\frac{\pi}{m}\,.$$

Here necessarily $\mu' = \lambda_{R'}$, since w is non-negative and, because of orthogonality of eigenfunctions, only an eigenfunction belonging to $\lambda_{R'}$ can be non-negative.
Approximately

$$\mu' \sim 1 - ch^2$$

where

$$c = \frac{\pi^2}{2a^2} + \frac{\pi^2}{2b^2}\,.$$

Taking suitable circumscribed and inscribed rectangles of R we see that λ is of the order $1 - ch^2$. This indicates that convergence of the iteration scheme is very slow for small h and hence that more refined methods for solving the difference scheme are called for.

Bibliography

1. Antosiewicz, H. A. and Gautschi, W., "Numerical methods in ordinary differential equations." In *Survey of Numerical Analysis*, ed. by John Todd, McGraw-Hill Book Co., 1962.
2. Antosiewicz, H. A. and Rheinboldt, C., "Numerical analysis and functional analysis, in *Survey of Numerical Analysis*, ed. by John Todd, McGraw-Hill Book Co., 1962.
3. Bodewig, E., *Matrix Calculus.* North Holland Publishing Co., 1959.
4. Collatz, L., *The Numerical Treatment of Difference Equations.* 3rd edition. Springer-Verlag, 1966.
5. Courant, R., Isaacson, E., Rees, M., "On the solution of nonlinear hyperbolic differential equations by finite differences," Comm. Pure Applied Math. 5 (1952), 243-256.
6. Courant, R., Friedrichs, K. O., and Lewy, H., "Über die partiellen Differentialgleichungen der mathematischen Physik." Math. Annalen 100 (1928), 32-74.
7. Courant, R., and Lax, P. D., "On nonlinear partial differential equations with two independent variables," Comm. Pure Applied Math. 2 (1949), 255-274.
8. Dahlquist, G., "Convergence and stability for a hyperbolic difference equation with analytic initial-values," Math. Scand. 2 (1954), 91-102.
9. Davis, P. J., *Interpolation and Approximation.* Ginn and Company, 1963
10. Douglas, J., Jr., and Rachford, H., "On the numerical solution of heat conduction problems in two and three space variables," Trans. Am. Math. Soc. 82 (1956), 421-439.
11. Forsythe, G. F. and Wasow, W. R., *Finite Difference Methods for Partial Differential Equations.* John Wiley and Sons, 1960.
12. Friedrichs, K. O., "Symmetric hyperbolic linear differential equations," Comm. Pure Applied Math. 7 (1954), 345-392.
13. Goldstine, H. H. and v. Neumann, J., "Numerical inverting of matrices of high order, II," Proc. Amer. Math. Soc. 2 (1951), 188-202.
14. Hardy, G. H., Littlewood, J. E., Polya, G., *Inequalities.* Cambridge Univ. Press, 1934.
15. Henrici, Peter, *Discrete Variable Methods in Ordinary Differential Equations.* Wiley and Sons, 1962.
16. Henrici, Peter, *Error Propagation for Difference Methods.* Wiley and Sons, 1962.
17. Hestenes, M. R. and Stiefel, E., "Methods of conjugate gradients for solving linear systems," J. Res. Nat. Bur. Standards 49 (1952), 409.
18. Hestenes, M. R., "The conjugate gradient method for solving linear systems,"

Numerical Analysis Proceedings of Symposium in Applied Mathematics, Vol. VI, McGraw-Hill Book Co., 1956.
19. Hildebrand, F. B., *Introduction to Numerical Analysis*. McGraw-Hill, 1956.
20. Hochstrasser, Urs, "Numerical methods for finding solutions of nonlinear equations." In *Survey of Numerical Analysis* (Editor, John Todd). McGraw-Hill Book Co., 1962.
21. Householder, Alston S., *Principles of Numerical Analysis*. McGraw-Hill, 1953.
22. Householder, Alston S., *The Theory of Matrices in Numerical Analysis*. Blaisdell, New York, 1964.
23. Isaacson, E. and Keller, H. B., *Analysis of Numerical Methods*. John Wiley and Sons, 1966.
24. John, F., "On integration of parabolic equations by difference methods," Comm. Pure Applied Math. 5 (1952), 155-211.
25. John, F., "Numerical solution of problems that are not well posed in the sense of Hadamard," Proceedings of the "Symposium on the numerical treatment of partial differential equations with real characteristics," organized by the Prov. Int. Computation Centre. Rome (1959), 103-116.
26. Kreiss, Heinz-Otto, "On difference approximations of the dissipative type for hyperbolic differential equations," Comm. Pure Applied Math. 17 (1964), 335-353.
27. Lax, P. D., "Numerical solution of partial differential equations," Am. Math. Monthly 72 (1965), No. 2, Part II (Herbert Ellsworth Slaught Memorial Papers), 74-83.
28. Lax, P. D. and Richtmyer, R. D., "Survey of stability of linear finite difference equations," Comm. Pure and Applied Math. 9 (1956), 267-293.
29. Lehmer, D. H., "A machine method for solving polynomial equations," J. Assoc. Comput. Mach. 8 (1961), 151-152.
30. Lewy, H., "On the convergence of solutions of difference equations." In *Studies and Essays Presented to R. Courant*. Interscience Publ., New York, 1948, pp. 211-214.
31. Milne, W. E., *Numerical Solution of Differential Equations*. John Wiley and Sons, 1953.
32. v. Neumann, J. and Goldstine, H. H., "Numerical inverting of matrices of high order," Bull. Am. Math. Soc. 53 (1947), 1021-1099.
33. Newman, Morris, "Matrix computation." In *Survey of Numerical Analysis*. (Editor, John Todd). McGraw-Hill Book Co., 1962.
34. Parlett, Beresford, "Accuracy and dissipation in difference schemes," Comm. Pure and Applied Math. 19 (1966), 111-113.
35. Richtmyer, R. D., *Difference Methods for Initial-Value Problems*. Interscience Publ., 1957.
36. Ritter, I. F., "The multiplicity function of an equation," Abstract, Bull. Am. Math. Soc. 63 (1957), p. 240.
37. Runge, C., "Über empirische Funktionen und die Interpolation zwischen äquidistanten Ordinaten," Zeitschrift für Mathematik und Physik 46 (1901), 224-243.
38. Taussky, Olga and Newman, Marvin, "Eigenvalues of finite matrices." In

Survey of Numerical Analysis (Editor, John Todd). McGraw-Gill Book Co., 1962.

39. Todd, John, "Classical numerical analysis." In *Survey of Numerical Analysis* (Editor, John Todd). McGraw-Hill Book Co., 1962.
40. Traub, J. F., *Iterative Methods for the Solution of Equations*. Prentice Hall, Inc. 1964.
41. Wasow, W., "On the truncation error in the solution of Laplace's equation by finite differences," J. Res. Nat. Bur. Standards, 48 (1952), 345-8.
42. Young, David M., "The numerical solution of elliptic and parabolic partial differential equations," In *Survey of Numerical Analysis* (Editor, John Todd). McGraw-Hill Book Co., 1962.

Index

Printed in Belgium